a pocketful of

RHYME

Imagination for a new generation

2006 Poetry Competition for 7-11 year-olds

YoungWriters

Devon & Cornwall
Edited by Annabel Cook

 Young**Writers**

First published in Great Britain in 2006 by:
Young Writers
Remus House
Coltsfoot Drive
Peterborough
PE2 9JX
Telephone: 01733 890066
Website: www.youngwriters.co.uk

SB ISBN 1 84602 589 3

Foreword

Young Writers was established in 1991 and has been passionately devoted to the promotion of reading and writing in children and young adults ever since. The quest continues today. Young Writers remains as committed to the nurturing of poetic and literary talent as ever.

This year's Young Writers competition has proven as vibrant and dynamic as ever and we are delighted to present a showcase of the best poetry from across the UK and in some cases overseas. Each poem has been selected from a wealth of *A Pocketful Of Rhyme* entries before ultimately being published in this, our fourteenth primary school poetry series.

Once again, we have been supremely impressed by the overall quality of the entries we have received. The imagination, energy and creativity which has gone into each young writer's entry made choosing the poems a challenging and often difficult but ultimately hugely rewarding task - the general high standard of the work submitted ensured this opportunity to bring their poetry to a larger appreciative audience.

We sincerely hope you are pleased with this final collection and that you will enjoy *A Pocketful Of Rhyme Devon & Cornwall* for many years to come.

Contents

Delabole Primary School, Delabole

Drake's Primary School, East Budleigh

Hayward's Primary School, Crediton

Charlotte Heywood (11) 45
Lucy Harris (10) 46
Rosie Porter (10) 46
Chloe Thresher (11) 47
Connor Wellington (10) 47
Alice Hornblower (10) 48
Brad Elliott (11) 48
Brandon McTigue (10) 49
Nathan Mew (11) 49
Glen Chudley (10) 50
Sean Goss (10) 51
Thomas Chapman (11) 52
Sophie-Lou Simpson (10) 52
Genevieve Chivers (9) 53
Ellie Stone (10) 53
Jasmine Hill (10) 54
Jack Lovering (10) 55

Heathcoat Primary School, Tiverton
Liam Ellacott (11) 55
Thomas Lilly D'Cruz (11) 56
John Savage (11) 56
Kelly-Jade Browning (10) 57
Enya Gooding (10) 57
Megan Scott (11) 58
Sophie Short (10) 58
Brandon Houldsworth (11) 59
Josh Ward (11) 59
Zoe Dickinson (10) 60
Lewis Hibbert (11) 60
Hal Kingston (11) 61
Shannon Collins (10) 61
Ethan Billing (10) 62
Alex Snell (11) 62
Ben Beaver (10) 63
Adam Bennett (11) 63
Jasmin Summers (11) 64
Taran Stevenson (11) 64
Katie Hales (11) 65
Louise Nash (11) 65
Joseph Zilch (11) 66

Tilly Oxenham Babb (10)   67
Aaron Young (11)   68

Keyham Barton RC Primary School, Keyham
Lloyd Marren (9)   68
Simon Sowden (9)   69
Naomi Hitchcock (9)   69
Holly May Clemens (9)   70
Jade Crotty (9)   71
Kayleigh Ward (9)   72

Lostwithiel School, Lostwithiel
Sam Thompson (11)   73
Megan Erwin & Rebecca Mortiboy (11)   74
Maxwell Davidson (10)   75
Piran Phippen & Jack Davidge (10)   76
Jordan Cummings (10)   77
Jacob Rickard (10)   78
Meghan Prindl (10)   79
Michael Sweet (10)   80
Amy Dunlap (11)   81
Thomas Mileham (11)   82
Simon Trebilcock (10)   83
Gabrielle Pedersen (11)   84
Rhyanah Kingston (10)   85
Johnathon Barnes (11)   86
Kyle Chapman (11)   87
Grace Edward-Collins (11)   88

Mithian School, St Agnes
Nessa Whitworth (11)   89
Ben Green (11)   90
Brittany Snook (11)   90
Serena Jones (10)   91
Josh Job (10)   91
Harry Waters (11)   92
Matt Wood (10)   92
Isabel Evans (10)   92
Olivia Richardson (10)   93

St Mary's RC School, Falmouth

St Peter's School, Lympstone

Thurlestone All Saints CE Primary School, Kingsbridge

The Poems

Do A Project

Play a piece on the piano
Add up a topic on maths
Suss out the tests in the splitting SATs
Scratch a project about a few rats

Try a bar of chocolate
Travel back to the Tudors
Throw up your hand and say
'Please Miss it's time for play.'

Blow up a bomb of World War II
Make your way back to the 50s
Write up a letter that you can send
Drive your teacher round the bend

Type a projection on ICT
Maybe cook a few cakes
Work hard to earn a few stickers
Or even the taste of a Snickers.

Run around the playground
Then go in for art
Why does Miss go on and on
Singing a really silly song?

Do your project on animals
Cartoons or
Do it on people
Or even St Paul's steeple

Practise your speech on a bit of French
Or even a bit of German
Miss just told me off for untying her bow
Now at last it's time to go.

Harriet Harvey (10)
Castle Primary School, Tiverton

Do A Topic

Design a project on art
Paint a picture on painting
Draw a topic on drawing
Sketch a project on sketching
Colour a picture on colouring
Shade a topic on shading

Blow up a project on science
Observe an experiment on observing changes,
Grow a topic on growing,
Move a project on movement,
Plant an experiment on plants and flowers,
Dissolve a topic on dissolving.

Eat a topic on healthy living,
Chew a project on vegetables,
Drink a topic on fizzy drinks,
Sip up a project on juice,
Stuff yourself with a topic of sweets.

Travel on a topic of travelling,
Fly on a project of aeroplanes,
Drive in a topic of cars,
Sail in a project of boats,
Walk in a topic of walking,
Cycle a project of bikes.

Be bored in a topic of school,
Get confused, in a project of science,
Read on a topic of reading,
Divide in a project of maths,
Type a topic of ICT,
Run a project of PE.

Danni-Marie Chant (11)
Castle Primary School, Tiverton

Star Wars

Strike down Vader from Star Wars
Burn up Anakin in Star Wars
Battle the Empire for the Republic
Take down the Jedi over the Sith
Rise up to be victorious
Train the child to become a Jedi
Become the best you can
Make The Force your own
Become better than Master Yoda
Join the dark side of The Force
Help the Rebels take down the Empire
Help the Clones take down the Droids
Fell to the Dark Side Anakin has
Take down the Sith for the Jedi
Make your mind, complete you must
Learn the way of The Force
Make the galaxy ours
Take over the Naboo System
You must learn to take down General Grievous
Discover the Dagobah System
Destroy the Death Star
The Empire is weak
You must help us
You are the only hope
Strike down the Empire
Destroy the Sith and restore peace
You are the chosen one
May The Force be with you.

Connor Barker (11)
Castle Primary School, Tiverton

Top Tips

Play a project on the violin
Or maybe even the piano
Carry a project with the Africans
Scream at a project in SATs
(And while you're at it
Mind you don't step the project on cowpats.)
Write a project in pencil
In pen
In chalk
Inside
Ride a project on horseback
Travel a project on trains
Blow up a project you really hate
And hope you won't be late
For school
For work
For your plane
These are my top tips for projects.

Hayley Kingdon (11)
Castle Primary School, Tiverton

Slip Slap

Slip, slap, pit-pat
Put a sandwich in my hat
KitKat, Walkers crisps
Ham Spam in my hands
Butter, flutter does it matter?
DT hall is really cool
Bang, crash with the pans
Splish-splosh with the dosh
Mitch match all the decimals
Patch up all my rap in our clubs after school.

Kimberley White (11)
Castle Primary School, Tiverton

Top-Up On Topic

Bomb a topic on WWII,
Run around on the topic of sport,
Go static with electricity,
Become psychic with the 80s,
Play a tribute to ACDC.

Go back in time when clocks were invented,
Divide a topic on maths,
Sail the project with the Vikings,
Write a project eating a sandwich.

Finish the project on the president's desk,
Climb up the Empire State Building,
Or the Eiffel Tower,
Drive a topic on cars,
Write a project today, tomorrow or yesterday.

Play the guitar, blow up Hitler and the Germans,
Be like Doctor Who.

Josh Hamidullah (11)
Castle Primary School, Tiverton

Do A Project

Scream and shout on a project on films
Throw a ball on a project on sport
Taste a treat on a project about food
Love the world on an RE report
Feel a material on a science report,
Spin a web on Charlotte's Web head,
Saw, draw on my door, what were learnt in the DT store,
Do take ten without a pen,
Bomb a topic on the World War II,
Invade and settle on the report about Vikings,
When we go to the PE hall,
We must remember to stay in school.

Paige Mitchell (11)
Castle Primary School, Tiverton

Cartoons

Do a project on cartoons
Do a project on all the characters
Small and big, pretty or ugly
Tall or short

Cuddle a project of cinnamorolls,
Battle a project of Badtz Marus,
Roller skate a project with Hello Kitty!
And live in the fantasy of Disney.

Be in the world of collecting Pokémon
Do a project of meeting new friends
Do a project of finding new creatures
In the forest, in the sea, in ghastly places,
Even in your back garden,
Defeat all the trainers with your fears,
But if you lose, you shall cry with tears.

Find the project of Disney
Hunt for the project of Mickey Mouse
Minnie Mouse, Goofy, Donald Duck
And last but not least, Pluto.

Play with the project of Rugrats
Protect the babies of Angelina
Fiddle with the project of Chuckie's hair,
Be in the group with the leader, Tommy.

Touch the screen of the project of 'Animal Crossing'.
Shake the trees, get stung by bees,
Or maybe find some money, or even a tiny spider,
Pay the project of your house to Tom Nook's
And even shop and sell there, catch the project of big or small fish
All different kinds, at night-time, at the seaside
Underneath the bridge, goodnight.

Serena Ng (11)
Castle Primary School, Tiverton

Final Fantasy VII

Do a project on Final Fantasy VII,
Do it on Red XIII's back,
Write it on Cloud's sword.

Do the project fighting Bahamat,
Do it killing Sephiroth,
Write on King Kak's crown.

Do the project driving Yazoo's bike,
Do it talking to Vincent,
Write it wearing Tofa's knuckles.

Do the project playing with Loz,
Do it spinning Sid's spear,
Write it laughing at Reno and Rude.

Do the project running from Shadow Hunters,
Do it looking at Lone Wolf,
Write it on Yuffie's blade.

Do the project in battle with Kadaji,
Do it daydreaming about Aeris,
Write it on your Barrett's gun.

Do the project in pain with G-graphic disease,
Do it protecting the president,
Write it on Genova's case.

Do the project on your hand,
Do it on someone's hand,
Write it wherever you please.

Samuel Lane (10)
Castle Primary School, Tiverton

Do A Project

Do a project on dinosaurs
The animals that stand up and roar
Have a top-up on topic
Move and mount in music,
Sail to the top of Vikings,
Soar and scream in singing,
Pick up a pencil, pen or colour to write, draw and doodle,
PE is the best, but you don't get a rest,
Whilst climbing and running about,
Eating and drinking, maybe a snack.
Education is important so don't sit back,
You need to learn and that is that,
Maybe a break is necessary, for us to play and laugh,
So don't be daft in science, as that's the way you'll fail.
When we learn French, although it may be Japanese,
We have to learn it, it wiggles in my knees.
Art is really cool, brushes, paint, water,
Although it can get messy, it really is fun!

Charlotte Pratt (11)
Castle Primary School, Tiverton

Do A Poem

Jump, kick, scream and shout,
Kick a ball, play about,
Do a poem that does rhyme,
Maybe a single line.
Click, bang, crunch, squirt,
Sometimes there might be a big alert.
But the sounds that we hear,
May sometimes appear,
Loud, quiet, big, small and tall,
We're all different after all,
Animals fly, crawl and lie
To try and catch their prey day after day.

Isabelle Hollis (11)
Castle Primary School, Tiverton

About A Project

Scream a project on a horror train, make it look like pain,
Screech a project on opera in the 70s,
Model a project with fashion and passion,
Wiggle a project with a big wiggly worm,
Pop with the beat,
Chill with the groovy gang,
Hit the beat with the meat,
Fight a project with bullying,
Kill a project with the murderer,
Swirl a project with a whirlwind,
Scatter a project with the leaves,
Spread a project on chocolate, on bread, in bed, on my head,
Stick a picture with materials,
Pick up the pastry from the bakery,
Dribble with your drink,
Suck a project on your Mint Imperials.

Gemma McArdle (10)
Castle Primary School, Tiverton

Do A Project

Shade in a drawing with charcoal
Paste on a picture with glue
Make a collage with materials
Create a poster too
Scribble on a book with pencils
Make a mask with wood
Write a story with a pen
I really think you should

Crunch all the projects on apples
Munch all the projects on carrots
Mash all the projects on bananas
Be sick on the projects on spinach.

Kasey Priscott (11)
Castle Primary School, Tiverton

Star Wars Project

Saber a topic on Star Wars
Strike down a Wookie on Star Wars
Battle the Trade Federation for the Republic,
Destroy the Sith and make the Jedi victorious,
Rise to the Empire and fall to the Rebel Alliance,
Become the best Jedi you can be,
Chase the wrong path to the Dark Side,
Chose the right to the Light Side.

Fall to the Sith, the clones have him, yes
Help the Gunguns reclaim their land,
Take down the Sith we must,
To use The Force, your mind must be clear,
Construct your light saber you must,
Prevent the Sith from taking the galaxy.

We must discover Dagobah System,
Protect the Millennium Falcon,
Or Han will have your head,
Experience the blow of the Death Star, a second time they will,
The Rebel Alliance is weak,
Ride Grievous' wheel bike
You must rely on Admiral Akbar,
Luke and Leia are our only hope,
Don't damage the Millennium Falcon,
Restore peace to the galaxy and
May The Force be with you!

Paul Urquhart (11)
Castle Primary School, Tiverton

Lessons

Muddle your paper with numbers,
Use all the different signs,
Addition, subtraction, divide
And the hardest - times.

Visit the history in books,
Travel to Ancient Greece,
Be Alexander the Great's right-hand man,
And travel the seven seas.

Light up the letters in literacy,
Write a discussion on the school fête,
Practise your boring old handwriting,
And don't forget the date.

Surf the net in ICT,
Or do a report on the sun,
Play lots of different PC games,
And have a lot of fun.

Top up your countries in topic,
Travel to Africa's country, Congo
Play with all the sweet children,
And play the lively bongo.

Slither your way to science,
Make your circuit the best,
Find out about the food and moons,
And get ready for the tests.

Molly Christian (11)
Castle Primary School, Tiverton

A Project

Kick a project on football
Bounce a topic on basketball
Throw a history on darts
Run a topic on athletics

Invade a topic on Vikings
Swim a topic on oceans
Taste a project on food
Sing a topic on Elvis

Tribute a topic to Queen and scream!
Write a project on paper, on wood,
On plaster casts,
And on fabric.

Draw a topic with a pencil,
With pen and ink,
Bomb a project on World War II,
Visit the history in York.

Travel a topic on trains,
Feel a project on materials,
Play a topic on music,
And divide a project on maths.

Rock a record,
Visit the 50s,
Bop the beat,
Screech the violin.

Fire a tank,
Destroy the Germans,
Stay at school if you're cool to,
Top up on topic!

Ben James (10)
Castle Primary School, Tiverton

Project

Embalm a project on the Egyptians
Sacrifice a dog for an Egyptian god
Creep into a pyramid
Find your mummy!
Not my mummy but someone who lived
Thousands of years BC
Sail on the Nile on a banana-shaped boat
Fall in the river praying to Raj
Type the project on the computer
Write it on paper
On papyrus
Go on a treasure hunt to find
Tutankhamen's gold
The teacher cheated,
It was only chocolate coins.

Bhushan Bailie (11)
Castle Primary School, Tiverton

Project

Swap a project on cards
Shoot a project on guns
Cut a project on knives,
Focus a project on The Force,
Cook a project on food,
Fix a project on a bike,
Bounce a project on a ball.
Burn a project on the fire,
Solve a project with a clue,
Build a project with a tower,
Laugh a project on a joke,
Sleep a project on your bed,
Find a project on some treasure,
Do a project on pencils and ink,
Do a project on your teacher,
Finish that project on the Greeks.

Matthew Waller (10)
Castle Primary School, Tiverton

My Time At School

Bomb a project on World War II
Swim a project in the sea
Draw a project on paint
Then have a cup of tea
Calculate a project on maths
One, two, three
Weave a project in string
How long can this be?
Drive a project on cars,
Plant a seed in flowers,
Peep at all the stars.
Read a project with a book,
Sing a note with a song,
Drink a project with water,
Bang a drum with a bong,
Draw a picture with some lead,
What can possibly go wrong?

Abigail Franklin Hackwood (11)
Castle Primary School, Tiverton

Project

Splash a project in a pool
Make a project on a cat
Fake a project about a hat
Fix a project on a bike
Cook a project on the sun
Hopefully it might be fun
Kick a project in a goal
Ride your project on a horse
Build a project on a house
Shake a project with a mouse
Play a project on the guitar
Hopefully it might go far
Burn a project on the fire
Do a project on the roof
And touch your project with your tooth.
Make a project on a beautiful day,
Now I have to go away.

Ciaran Butcher (10)
Castle Primary School, Tiverton

Our School Life

Invade and bomb the Vikings
Settle down and paint their sinking ships
Divide and add the nasty maths
With all the numbers jumping around
But there's only one problem
Eight ate the nine
Not a healthy snack as nine is high in sugar
Sing and shout and ache your mouth
The teachers say, 'Settle down for your test today.'
Science breaks our flesh and bones
Now our knees are joined with our toes
PE jumps around in our minds,
But OK it's a life of grime
ABC hit it,
Do literacy with no capital letters along with full stops!
The other day we had SATs which means
Sing Aloud Teachers Say!

Jasmine Brace (11)
Castle Primary School, Tiverton

Somewhere In The World

Somewhere in the world today, another person dies
Another child left lonely among the worried cries,
Poppies help the family and the forgotten wives,
To help to rebuild their frightful scared lives.
People all over, have one minute's silence to remember
Those who died
They lay wreaths in towns and in streets to remember winning the war!

David Fisher (10)
Crowan Primary School, Camborne

Rap About Food

You can rap about food
When you're really in a mood
You can rap about sweets
When you really want a treat
You can rap about bananas
When you're in your pink pyjamas
You can rap about ice cream
When you're slapping on suncream
You rap about a pea
When you're sitting having your tea
You can rap about a curry
When you're really in a hurry
You can rap about grapes
When you're wearing a pink cape
You can rap about pasta
When you're running even faster
You can rap about dates
When you're really, really late
You can rap about food
When you're really in the mood!

Jodie Richards (11)
Crowan Primary School, Camborne

Remembrance Day

Remembrance Day the march begins
Remembrance Day the poppies bring
Remembrance Day the wreaths are laid
Remembrance Day some lives are saved
Remembrance Day the silence starts
Remembrance Day their lives are gone
Remembrance Day they sing a song
Remembrance Day has been and gone!

Paige Ansell (11)
Crowan Primary School, Camborne

Remembrance Day

Somewhere in the world today a ceremony is heard, today
Somewhere in the world today a family are moving, today
Somewhere in the world today a man is wearing his medals
                              with pride, today
Somewhere in the world today a poppy is being worn, today
Somewhere in the world a family are all together.

Stevie Tolcher (10)
Crowan Primary School, Camborne

Mix It And Make It

A wart from a witch's nose
A wing from a vampire bat
Three deadly evil mice
A rattle of a skeleton's bones
A groan from an old spectre
An ugly devil from Hell
An eyeball from a spooky spirit
Nine howls from a werewolf
A horn of a Minotaur
Mix it and make it
The soup will be delightful.

Lois Pengelly (11)
Crowan Primary School, Camborne

The Perfect Teacher

I think there's something you should know
That you make school a fun place to go
I come every day to learn something new
I have a great time 'cause I'm taught by you
I'm sure it's agreed by every pupil in the school,
That having you teach is totally cool!

Emma Winder (11)
Crowan Primary School, Camborne

Firework

Extending, bright, fizzing light
Fills the midnight sky
Up in the air we don't care if we don't say goodbye
Zooming high, wailing in the sky
Showing a fire-like glow
I don't know why they show their bursting coloured glow
Rainbow-bright against the shimmering moon
The bursting pop does stop
At exactly half-past ten
But next year it will start again.

Elizabeth Weston (10)
Crowan Primary School, Camborne

A Troll Under Your Bed

Do you ever have the feeling
There's a troll under your bed?
Because if you don't I'll tell you
Now there's one sleeping by your head
Oops! I think you woke him, he
Doesn't think you're there!
He's out for some food
He's walking to the chair,
Quick, get back in bed, he's coming back to you!
Oops! A bit too late I think, now he's got you!

Martha Hilliard (9)
Crowan Primary School, Camborne

Bonfire Night

Rainbow, whizzing, zooming
Fizzing, vivid bright colours
Sparkling light, extremely bright
The night sky raging with rockets.

Joshua Blewett (10)
Crowan Primary School, Camborne

The Months

January's bleak,
Ice-cold hits your face
From the frosty leaves.

June's summer,
Heat pours on the beach,
Steam lollies dripping.

Bitter cold winds knock,
Warmth pours out from hot chocolate,
Red fireworks explode.

Snowman in a field
Waiting for raindrops to fall,
Ice drops from leaves.

Eden Pitt (10)
Crowan Primary School, Camborne

Don't Look

If you're lying in your bed
With the covers on your head
I'll tell you now, not to look
There's a monster over there
Sitting on your old, creaky chair
He's glaring right at you now,
No, don't look
Oh no, too late!
He's coming to get you now
You can't escape.

Kimberley Taylor (11)
Crowan Primary School, Camborne

Omaha Beach

A deadly battle
A horrible day
A silent memorial
A dead army
A horrifying war
A bloody sea
A sad person
A horrible death
A dead soldier
A sad wife
A brave soldier
A world saved.

Ahren Warwick (11)
Crowan Primary School, Camborne

The Shark

A deadly silence
A bone breaker
A leg linger
A flesh biter
A blood sniffer
A fin kicker
A people scarer
A teethy terror
A sharp swimmer
A fast fish
A head eater.

Lewis Adams (10)
Crowan Primary School, Camborne

The Magic Box

(Based on 'Magic Box' by Kit Wright)

I will put in my box . . .

The feeling of touching a spider,
A snake curled around my neck,
A bird perched on a tree's arm.

I will put in my box . . .

The crunch of a hyena scavenging a rotten bone
The buzz buzz of a bee in a busy nest
Splash! As the fish falls into a pond.

I will put in my box . . .

The sight of a joey in its mother's pouch
Seeing a monkey swing from tree to tree
A thorny lizard crawling on a log.

I will put in my box . . .

A zebra drinking from a lush waterfall,
An anteater scoffing the scurrying red ants,
A puffing toad breathing fresh air.

I will put in my box . . .

The smell of a muddy pig,
A bear's scent wafting to my nose
An aye-aye marking its territory.

My box is fashioned from animal fur and reptiles' scales
With eagles, sharp talons
The hinges are the beaks of birds.

I shall play with pets in
My box on the high mountains
Of Mexico and run back down
To the golden desert,
The colour of the sun.

Oliver Leach (10)
Delabole Primary School, Delabole

The Magic Box

(Based on 'Magic Box' by Kit Wright)

I will put in the box ...
A taste of a flickering flame,
The bitterness of saltpans all around,
And the fruitilicious mangoes from the village.

I will put in the box . . .
The touch of an autumn fire,
Or a stroke of a slithering snake,
And a tickle of a star's first night.

I will put in the box . . .
Three golden wishes wrapped up in silk,
My brother sitting in a tree,
Or butterfly wings swaying in the breeze.

I will put in my box . . .
Five pink polka-dot pandas in a potato tree,
A holiday destination on Pluto,
And an alien car with square wheels.

My box is fashioned from bones and skulls,
With fire on the lid and chants in the corners,
Its hinges are the jaws of a great white.

I shall glide in my box,
Over the African plains,
Then fall on a skyscraper,
The colour of the wind.

Eliza Burnard (10)
Delabole Primary School, Delabole

My Africa Poem

I wish I could see
The flickering forms of a campfire
Or the shining staggered stars lost in the night sky.

I wish I could feel,
The crumbling bark of an ancient life,
With the sharpest leaves.

I wish I could hear,
The growl of a many striped tiger,
With an injured leg.

I wish I could smell,
The freshly grown herbs,
Grown in the arable mud.

I wish I could taste,
The mixed spice,
With the shiny red chilli.

Marcus Taylor (9)
Delabole Primary School, Delabole

I Wish I Could . . .

I wish I could taste
The sweetened flavour of a pickled pepper
I wish I could smell
The flame of a Japanese fireball
I wish I could touch
The spiky spine of a scaly lizard
I wish I could hear
The loud roar of a speedy cheetah
I wish I could see
A lion tearing the flesh from an antelope.

Daniel Van Nuil (9)
Delabole Primary School, Delabole

Things I Have Been Doing Lately

Going in goal when I play football
Staring at the TV
Bouncing on my trampoline
Arguing with my brother and sister
Picking up a deadly snake
Holding a newt
Sprinting with my dogs
Playing with my PlayStation
Picking a new basketball from Asda
Looking after my cat
Sprinting to the park
Painting my house
Begging for pocket money
Riding on my bike.

Mac Irwin (10)
Delabole Primary School, Delabole

The Five Senses

I wish I could see
The lions in the scorching sun
Having their afternoon sleep

I wish I could feel
The crumbling bark of an old oak tree

I wish I could smell
The magnificent soup and oranges on the stalls.

I wish I could hear
The laugh that a hyena makes.

I wish I could taste freshly cooked antelope
From an African.

Eleanor Randall (8)
Delabole Primary School, Delabole

The Magic Box

(Based on 'Magic Box' by Kit Wright)

I will put in the magic box . . .

The sight of an Olympic swimmer,
Swimming with the deadliest shark in the world.
Lions roaring as they eat the juicy flesh of a deer,
Dolphins chirping and laughing at each other.

I will put in the magic box . . .

The sound of wolves howling at the white and bright moon.
A piranha chomping and snapping on a dead fish.

I will put in the magic box . . .

The smell of burnt chicken from a roast dinner
And yellow corn about to grow in the dusty field.

I will put in the magic box . . .

The touch of seaweed that slithers through the gaps of my fingers.

I will put in the magic box . . .

The taste of burnt flames that just fall from the sky,
And a circled shape snake.

My box is fashioned from animal skin and the trunk of an elephant,
The hinges are made from sharp teeth.

I shall play games on a hill in France in my box
And then sprint home again at sunset.

Jordan Blanchard (10)
Delabole Primary School, Delabole

The Magic Box

(Based on 'Magic Box' by Kit Wright)

I will put in the magic box . . .
The taste of a banana that just fell from the tree
The taste of a zebra that a lion just killed

I will put in the magic box . . .
The amazing sight of a chameleon always changing colour
The beautiful sight of butterflies' wings

I will put in the magic box . . .
Five golden wishes
The hope that Great Gran will live a few years at least
A beautiful picture that an artist has painted.

I will put in the magic box . . .
A flying pig swooping down on people,
A lamp zooming across the air,
A flame inside ice and the ice has never melted a bit.

My box is fashioned from flames and ice and gold
With a piece of the sun as a lid
And its hinges are made of human bones.

I shall snowboard in my box,
On Mount Everest, snowboarding all day, just to get to the bottom,
And land with no snow at all.

Alex Hewitt (10)
Delabole Primary School, Delabole

The African Box

(Inspired by 'Magic Box' by Kit Wright)

I will put in the box . . .
The touch of an African drum
And the feel of a tiger's coat
Or a spread of a snake's skin.

I will put in the box . . .
The sight of a girl helping her mum
And a boy with a disease ready to die
Or a girl walking ten miles to get water.

I will put in the box . . .
The splash of water coming out of the wells,
And flowers coming out of the ground,
Or more medicine in the doctors and hospitals.

I will put in the box . . .
The last piece of food in their mouth,
And the last tablet of medicine to help a boy,
Or the last time you would ever see him live.

I will put in the box . . .
The sound of infants clapping with the drums,
And the corn growing in fields,
Or children having fun at school.

I will put in the box . . .
A well rolling in the village,
Or an elephant rolling in muddy water,
And children having brightly separated classes.

The box is fashioned,
The box is covered with leopard skin,
And the hinges are made by rhino's toenails,
The lead is covered with snakeskin.

Yasmin Woodward (10)
Delabole Primary School, Delabole

African Wish

(Inspired by 'Magic Box' by Kit Wright)

I will put in the box . . .
The touch of an African tie-dye robe against my skin
And the smooth coat of goat skin
Or a small bird landing on my shoulder.

I will put in the box . . .
The sight of waving corn across a bone-dry savannah
And the flurry of crows coming to nest.

I will put in the box . . .
A great wish of more medical help for restless souls,
And the aid of every spirit,
And the beat of the drums as the dancers whirl.

I will put in the box . . .
A river trickling through the town backwards,
And a mountain of warm clothing and food
Or no disease or harm.

My box is fashioned,
With snake skin and tiger stripes
The lid is decorated with fish scales.
Its hinges are the teeth of 'great whites'.
And the corners are made of pure gold.

I shall dance in the box
All the way around the world
And back again . . .
The box will be hidden in the rainforest
And no one will find it.

Courtney Hill (9)
Delabole Primary School, Delabole

Africa Life

The feel of the African sand between my toes,
So dry, so hot,
Why is it not wet, why not?
Is it because there is no rain?
To the Africans this must be a pain.

The sight of the symbols of the African tribes,
Giving to me some excellent vibes,
Making me feel warm inside.
Looking at them I almost cried,
Not because I was sad, but I was feeling great,
If I could, I would have eight.

The sound of a herd of elephants,
A baby and his mum calling to the dad
One of the best experiences I have ever had.

The taste of sunshine against my tongue,
Like hot chocolate, yum-yum

The smell of the spices the widows sell for a living,
Poor, unfortunate people, they're practically giving,
The prices are so low,
A week's money could just buy you your dinner.

Sam Leach (9)
Delabole Primary School, Delabole

I Wish

I wish I could see the golden lions,
Blazing in the scorching sunset on the hilltop,
Or the elephants stomping on the green, smooth grass

I wish I could hear the children singing,
Dancing in the gazing hot sun.

I wish I could taste the sweet fruit melting in my mouth
I wish I could smell a freezing raindrop
I wish I could touch the hyena eating.

Charlotte Benson (9)
Delabole Primary School, Delabole

I Wish

I wish I could see
The growling lions lying in the sun
Or roughly chasing wildebeest

I wish I could hear
The voices of the black people in
The markets of Wagadogo
Or maybe listen to the tweeting birds.

I wish I could taste
The lovely sweet taste of the food
Or even make some.

I wish I could touch
The dry, dusty sand in the deserts
Or make dust castles.

I wish I could smell
The sweet scent of the scorching, lovely sun
Or the air.

Ray Galley (9)
Delabole Primary School, Delabole

I Will Put In The Box . . .

(Inspired by 'Magic Box' by Kit Wright)

I will put in the box . . .
A golf player on the green grass
I will put in the box . . .
The smell of a rose flower
And a diamond dandelion
I will put in the box . . .
Honey taste on a toffee rock.
I will put in the box . . .
A cutting chug of Ashley's mower
And a go-kart with a lion on the front.

Zak Harris (10)
Delabole Primary School, Delabole

Refugee

I see the guns
The frightening flash
I want to leave
My dad won't let me
I run away
The border is near
I can see it
It is open
I run
I try to get through
But the soldiers close the border
I shout and beg, I need to get through
I say to them
My family
Gone
My home
Gone
I have nowhere to go.

Kierron Dinsdale (10)
Drake's Primary School, East Budleigh

Walking

I hear the pistol shooting,
I'm walking, I'm walking
Somebody screams and gets dragged away,
I'm walking, I'm walking
I'm scared what will happen next
I'm walking, I'm walking
My brothers are gone
I'm walking, I'm walking
I'm all alone,
I'm walking, I'm walking.

Georgia Harwood (10)
Drake's Primary School, East Budleigh

I'm A Soldier

They're all around
Everywhere I go they're there
Everywhere I look they're stood there,
Homeless, no food, nothing, they're just stood there,
Trembling with fear,
They are shrieking and howling saying, 'Help me.'
It's so tragic,
I'm stood there at the gate, I don't know what to do,
Whether to let them through or to just leave them there,
It's a hard decision,
Should I run and hide
Or leave them stood there starving?
With nowhere to go, I need to help them
But should I?

Lia Taylor (11)
Drake's Primary School, East Budleigh

Refugee

I ran
The sounds of guns in my ears
Then I heard the noise I feared,
The rumble of bombs.
The guns drowned by the sound of planes and bombs,
These were the sounds of war.

I was forced to flee,
I was forced to be a refugee,
Nowhere to be,
No one to see,
That's what I was,
A refugee,
No one to see,
No one to be,
That's a refugee . . . that's me.

Jay Brogan (10)
Drake's Primary School, East Budleigh

A Long Journey, But For What?

People screaming everywhere
My dad is bleeding, quick
Get a cloth,
To mop up the blood,
His eyes are shut, but
He's not asleep.

Mum's rushing around the house,
Gathering my brother and sister,
Everybody's screaming now,
As soldiers raid our home.

I've decided I'm going,
Off to find a safe place,
Maybe my mum's there,
Maybe even Dad.

I've been walking for several days now,
My feet feel like I've been walking on hot coal,
Others are dying all around me,
But I don't know a single soul.

We can see the border now,
Around it are more soldiers,
Have I made the right decision?
Someone tell me, please.

They've let a few people in,
But turned me away,
Now I'm on some aircraft,
Flying home again.

Zoë Thomas (11)
Drake's Primary School, East Budleigh

Every Step's A Mile

We've left now, we can't go back
Searching, trying to find the border
Every step seems a mile away
I hear my little brother crying
'How much longer?'

We're alone, it's me and him against the world,
We're too young this shouldn't happen, not now, not yet, not ever
The bombs are loud and so is the crowd.

I wish the ground would swallow me up
But I've got to stay strong for him,
I wish it would go, I wish it would,
Maybe, maybe if I dream it will end.

No, that doesn't work,
I pray, I search, please help me Lord,
Why is my life so tough?
I just wish we reach the camp before it's too late.

There's the light ahead of me, it's the camp
Yes, we made it.
We, I mean me and my brother
We remember those who have died
And those who have loved and lost
We were lucky really.

Katie Ralph (11)
Drake's Primary School, East Budleigh

Bang!

I see them running, running towards me
Their faces display one emotion, scared
Men, women, children, babies and old people
Some carrying what seems like their whole house,
They're closer now, some have reached the barriers,
Some are crying in tears of sadness,
Others in tears of happiness,
I can hear their voices screaming, 'Please let us in.'

They start to push and punch us
We have to stop them coming in
One man's starting to throw stones at me
Bang! He was shot by someone . . .
It was me.

Ben Gould-Smith (10)
Drake's Primary School, East Budleigh

Help Me

Help me, I'm trapped
I can't get out
There are people in green,
They won't let me out.

I need a home,
I need food,
I need water,
I need clothes,
I am really scared.

I hear gun noises that I don't like,
Will it be me next?
Will I be killed?

Rhona Hunter (10)
Drake's Primary School, East Budleigh

I'm Alone

Who's that,
Coming towards the house?
Trucks barging in,
Threatening faces,
Guns loaded.

I call for Mum
But I get no answer,
I'm awake and everyone's asleep
Or are they!

My eyes are closed
Wishing for hope
Thinking of a life
That I shall not live again.

Gina Bentley (11)
Drake's Primary School, East Budleigh

The Guard

Will they come, will they?
How many without a home?
Will they give them food?
How will they get through?
Will they have a home?
Will there be ill ones?
How many children are there without parents?
I hope I don't get involved.

Frank Reed (11)
Drake's Primary School, East Budleigh

The Life Of A Refugee

Nowhere to live
Nowhere to go

My village destroyed
The camp crowded
Forced to leave home
I must catch a boat
My one chance

The borderline is near,
I'm close, I'm close
But wait, a soldier stops the boat,
He asks why we're here,
I tell,
We can't go in,
We're forced to camp outside the borderline.

Other boats pass,
Get in with no trouble,
A ferry,
I must sneak on.

I'm in the country,
No.
The ferry stops,
It must have arrived at the docks.
There's a lorry, on I get.

But there's a soldier,
He stops and inspects the lorry.
He catches me,
Then forces me to camp with the others,
Or I get shot.

The life of a refugee,
I'd prefer to drown . . . help me please.

Reuben Neilan (9)
Drake's Primary School, East Budleigh

Survival

Nothing left
No home
You only get one chance in life
No Mum to kiss goodnight
No Dad to bring home food
No brothers to play with
No sisters to hear laughing
No one to love
No one to care for
Life's not fair.

Louise West (10)
Drake's Primary School, East Budleigh

My Cat

He snuggles up to me at night,
With a smile on his face,
Also when he is figuring out a case.

Whether it's hunting for bees,
Or climbing trees,
He's always feeling happy.

He's funnier than a clown
And always falling down
And making us laugh.

He's always there to make you have joy
And always plays with his toys,
Whenever and wherever he wants.

He sleeps on the mat,
He is my cat
And a lovely one he is.

Chelsea Lander (11)
Hayward's Primary School, Crediton

Speed

Speed is moving through the streets as fast as you can,
Speed is fast and slow,
Speed is the wheels on a bike spinning round and round,
Speed is the Earth rotating around on its axis,
Speed is a tennis ball reaching speeds up to 150mph,
Speed is the time of our much appreciated lives,
Speed is time,
Speed is a 1000bhp Borgetti Varon,
Speed is the time it took the tsunami to destroy the
Whole of Sri Lanka and its people's lives,
Speed is global warming taking its pace,
Speed is frightening,
Speed is mph,
Speed is the difference of writing and speaking,
Speed is death and life,
Speed is the time you spend in school to get a good education,
Speed is . . .
Speed is . . .
Speed is . . .
Speed is . . .
Speed is . . .
Speed!

Lewis Easterbrook (11)
Hayward's Primary School, Crediton

Kennings Gymnastics

Handstand-archer,
Round off-flicker,
Met-somersaulter,
Vault-balancer,
Fast-frog leaper,
Bridge-flipper,
Trampoline-diver,
Medal-winner.

Alexis Jones (10)
Hayward's Primary School, Crediton

I'm Climbing Trees

I'm climbing trees
And watching bees.

Up I go,
To continue the flow.

I'm falling down,
With a frown.

On the floor,
Mum opens the door.

I'm now indoors,
My dad's on the moors.

I don't want to be a clown,
But my tree fell down.

Jade Walters (11)
Hayward's Primary School, Crediton

My Day Out

Trout, salmon, flounder, perch,
I'll ride my minibike into church,
Dace, tuna, haddock, cod,
Wait till you hear the minister shout.

Fish, fish, fish, fish, fish, fish.

Plaice, swordfish, sucker, eel,
I'll race my father in his automobile,
Herring, flounder, bluegill, shark,
We'll race all day till after dark.

Luke Pearce (11)
Hayward's Primary School, Crediton

The Crazy Grandma

She's standing on the edge,
She's 56,
She's crazy and free,
She's my granny,
Me, Lottie and Rachel, embarrassed as ever,
Faces bright red,
She's freaky,
She's wahoo-ing,
She's old-ish.

What *crazy* old lady would bungee-jump?
Have you ever met one that would?
My gran is fun and exciting,
But the worst thing is,
She's embarrassing.

Hannah Tucker (11)
Hayward's Primary School, Crediton

Sunset

Small hands,
Touching wet sand.

Orange clouds,
Like many shrouds.

Pink sky,
Like a pig that can fly.

The sea is rising.

Crashing waves,
Falling.

Whistling whales,
Calling.

Joanna Cartwright (11)
Hayward's Primary School, Crediton

Football Crazy

I sleep,
I eat,
I drink
And dream football.

My dream would be to play with Defoe,
Pass, shoot,
Score past Robinson
And play tactics.

Attack the ball,
Crowd cheering you on,
Nervous but calm,
We're winning, *hooray!*

Score a goal,
Offside,
Argue with ref,
Red, sent off.

Katy Harkness (11)
Hayward's Primary School, Crediton

Pig

Bacon maker,
Mud roller,
Pink oinker,
Piglet styer,
Grub eater,
Slop swimmer,
Muddy animal,
Market seller,
Pork creator,
Piggy grunter.

Livy Griffiths (11)
Hayward's Primary School, Crediton

Wings

If I had wings
I would fly to the moon,
For all the light,
Like a light lamp.

If I had wings,
I would fly to space,
To see all the plants,
Like colours of the rainbow.

If I had wings,
I would fly to Greece,
Where the waters splash,
Like thunder crashing on the floor.

If I had wings,
I would fly around the world,
To see the beautiful countries
Around the world.

If I had wings,
I would swim through the clouds,
Like swimming in water,
In the swimming pool.

If I had wings,
I would fly to everywhere and anywhere,
To find out everything,
In the universe.

Shannen Waldron (11)
Hayward's Primary School, Crediton

Flying Through Space

If I could fly,
I would go to the stars,
See all the planets, Jupiter and Mars.

If I could fly,
I would go to eat the moon's cheese,
Thank God it's not made from peas.

If I could fly,
I would go to Mars,
Is it really made from chocolate bars?

If I could fly,
I would zoom through the sky,
Passing planets as I went by.

If I could fly,
I would love to touch the sky,
It would be better than the taste of pie.

If I could fly,
I would see shooting stars,
They could be space cars.

If I could fly,
I would go to the space dome,
After the excitement I would go home.

Charlotte Heywood (11)
Hayward's Primary School, Crediton

The River

Whoosh! I'm free,
Free to roar down the mountain,
Like a lion after his prey.

Crash! I'm deafening,
I'm louder than a thousand trumpets,
Booming through the valley.

Help! I'm dangerous,
I'm as deadly as a sandstorm,
Raging through the desert.

Swish! I'm magic,
I'm a wonder of the Earth,
Through my journey out to sea.

Lucy Harris (10)
Hayward's Primary School, Crediton

Gibbons

Trunk climber,
Branch clasper,
Twig swinger,
Rope hanger,
Tail curler,
Territory protector,
Aggressive fighter,
Fruit muncher,
Flea finder,
Kind nature.

Rosie Porter (10)
Hayward's Primary School, Crediton

Falling

I stand on the edge,
More scared than ever,
The door opens,
I stand there, looking down!

I am nervous,
But I jump!
I pass clouds,
Big fluffy ones.

I tugg the cord,
My parachute opens,
I'm floating down,
Further and further!

I feel as free as a bird,
Light as a feather,
The breeze against my face,
Up my nose, in my mouth!

I touch the ground gently,
It was great,
I will never forget!
Never!

Chloe Thresher (11)
Hayward's Primary School, Crediton

Invasion Of The Rainforest

A storm was approaching,
Black clouds scudded up from the south,
An ink-black sky stretched for miles,
Fork-like lightning prodded the forest gloom,
The machine-like monster terrorises,
Driving animals to the corners of the forest.

Connor Wellington (10)
Hayward's Primary School, Crediton

Dad

When one is overcome by death,
As she or he draws one last breath,
Their life flashes from where they're born,
Then later on their mourners mourn.

Be it Auntie, Uncle, Dad,
For lifelong we will be sad
And remember, that one day,
We'll see this poem a different way.

After all, when people get old,
People die, it's been long foretold,
We must remember they're just asleep,
Falling deeper, deeper, deep.

Alice Hornblower (10)
Hayward's Primary School, Crediton

My Puppy

Small runner,
Quick swimmer,
Desperate eater,
Squeaky barker,
Mini jumper,
Cat chaser,
Rabbit hunter,
Nasty biter,
Back garden fighter,
Ball chaser.

Brad Elliott (11)
Hayward's Primary School, Crediton

If I Had Wings

(Based on 'If I had Wings' by Pie Corbett)

If I had wings,
I would glide past noisy houses.

If I had wings,
I would soar past crashing meteors.

If I had wings,
I would whizz to Mercury with my acid-proof coat.

If I had wings,
I would flutter up to ice-cold Saturn.

If I had wings,
I would visit the shadowy moon.

If I had wings,
I would go and dive in the skies.

Brandon McTigue (10)
Hayward's Primary School, Crediton

The Supersonic Storm

Leaves began to spin and crackle,
Fiery-red orang-utan chews his dinner,
Thunder echoes like a lion's roar,
Tall trees tremble,
First raindrops biting down like lion's teeth,
Lightning rips through the chalk-black sky,
A branch is shredded free and smashes down,
A roar of thunder signals for a stop,
Then all quiet, the final whistle had gone.

Nathan Mew (11)
Hayward's Primary School, Crediton

Skydiving

Totally weightless,
Falling at a blinding speed,
Through the huge splash of blue paint,
Which is the sky.

I float freely,
In a cold rush of air,
Flying past the drifting sheep that
Look like clouds.

It's an unforgettable experience,
But then the storm begins.

A thunder crack,
A flash of lightning,
The wind hurls me thousands of miles,
From where I was.

But then the storm stops,
The huge cloud of grey above,
Becomes a vast ocean of blue,
With cloud-shaped waves,
Crashing into the horizon.

The grey thunderclouds transform
Into hovering lambs,
Feasting on the blue fields.

I fall gently onto an expanse,
Of lush, lime-coated grass.

Glen Chudley (10)
Hayward's Primary School, Crediton

Touch The Sky

If I could glide through the sky,
I would weightlessly float in a puddle of blue,
Feeling sick in the gut as I tumble to the tip of the sea,
Ecstatic until the storm comes.

If I could glide through the sky,
The storm beating down on me
And I hopelessly hover over the fields,
Flimsy like a plastic ruler.

If I could glide through the sky,
The lightning strikes just behind me,
A thunder clap echoing through the sky,
As the foamy white clouds crash,
Into the stony grey thunderclouds.

If I could glide through the sky,
Suddenly the storm stops
And I float free as a bird,
Through the light blue sky.

If I could glide through the sky,
I open my parachute,
I am flexible as elastic,
As my feet touch the ground,
The unbelievable experience,
Finally ends.

Sean Goss (10)
Hayward's Primary School, Crediton

If I Could Drive

If I could drive through space,
I would visit every planet.

If I could drive through space,
I would drive as fast as I can
And feel the wind glide through my hair.

If I could drive through space,
I would taste the moon,
As cold as a glacier.

If I could drive through space,
I would count every
Single shining star.

If I could drive through space,
I would gaze at the creatures,
As I drive past.

If I could drive through space,
I would dream of flying an aeroplane,
From Earth to Neptune.

Thomas Chapman (11)
Hayward's Primary School, Crediton

Who Am I?

Grass muncher,
Beef maker.

Mess creator,
Milk shaker.

Tail swayer,
Cow pooer.

Eye glistener,
Loud mooer.

Sophie-Lou Simpson (10)
Hayward's Primary School, Crediton

Dancing The Skies

If I could dance the skies,
I would swoop round and feel I had power over the air,
I would fly to the ends of the Earth and beyond.

If I could dance the skies,
I would be the most powerful person in the world,
I would be host to the wonderful weird sensation of flying.

If I could dance the skies,
I would take a piece of cloud and create my own weather,
I would leap over Africa and jump over New Zealand.

If I could dance the skies,
I would feel weightless walking on the seas,
I would have the amazing power to skip on the air.

If I could dance the skies,
When the magical day ended,
I would settle on a cloud and rest in the breeze.

Genevieve Chivers (9)
Hayward's Primary School, Crediton

If I Could Swim Through An Empty Sky

If I could swim through an empty sky,
I would feel fantastic feelings fly by
And see sensational views down low and up high.

If I could swim through an empty sky,
I would zoom to planets unknown
And bring joy to the people on Earth.

If I could swim through an empty sky,
I would feel amazingly high but to some very low
And even to some in-between.

If I could swim through an empty sky,
I would realise I am the only one of my kind
And feel all alone.

Ellie Stone (10)
Hayward's Primary School, Crediton

Fly Free

Magically falling through clouds of white,
Weightlessly flying through a sea of nothingness,
Freely moving, not a soul in sight,
Powerless to do anything but fly.

Amazing, breathtaking views,
Powerful in my own way,
Drifting through flocks of sheep,
Unbelievably free from the planet of complaints.

A storm is brewing, in control,
Petrified by its magnificent power,
Paralysed by its strength,
Sprinting winds chasing me.

Horrified by electric patterns,
Scared by beating of a drum,
Frightened by teardrops,
Boulders being hurled at me.

Want to stop and give up,
But I've got to keep going,
Determination keeps nagging,
My parachute has opened.

Unexpected storm calming,
Wish I could do it again,
Time to go home now,
Journey coming to an end.

Jasmine Hill (10)
Hayward's Primary School, Crediton

Free As A Bird

Unforgettably magical,
Rushing through the skies,
Looking down at the patchwork quilt of fields below,
Unbelievably fast.

Speeding down,
Towards the Earth,
Wishing this would never end,
Opening my parachute . . .
Aaaahhh!

Giant gusts of wind,
Clouds whipping at my clothes,
With their frozen hands,
As cold as ice,
Powerlessly struggling in their grip.

The winds easing,
Cracking hands melting away,
Coming down to Earth again,
Down,
Down,
Down,
Down.

Jack Lovering (10)
Hayward's Primary School, Crediton

Hammerhead Shark Began

He took a thousand sharpened swords for his teeth,
For his fins, he stole the moon and he tore the wings off the hawk.
From the jungle he swiped the snake's tongue,
Then at night, he took the thaws hammer for his head,
He used the snake's old skin for his own.

Liam Ellacott (11)
Heathcoat Primary School, Tiverton

Python Was Born

(Based on 'Cat Began' by Andrew Matthews)

He took the softness of the snow and the shape
Of the gleaming moon;
He also took the ice from
The caves to make its scaly skin.

He took the blood of its victims, the salt of sea
And the scent of death to make its deadly poison.

He took the shape of a fork to make its sharp tongue
And it stole the dunes from the desert to
Make its deadly, sensitive tongue.

He ripped the fins off the sharks to make its destructive fangs.
It took the shape of the
Mountain tops to make its fangs.

He took the darkness of the night and the glitter
Of the sun to make its blinding eyes.
That's how the python was born.

Thomas Lilly D'Cruz (11)
Heathcoat Primary School, Tiverton

Naughty Little Pixie

I'm a pixie very, very small,
I can steal things from the mall,
Here and there and everywhere,
I am smaller than a pear.

I live in a toadstool,
I love playing with my bouncy ball,
But the only problem is,
I am too small!

John Savage (11)
Heathcoat Primary School, Tiverton

Horse

(Based on 'Cat Began' by Andrew Matthews)

The birth of Horse,
For her coat,
She stole the softness of cotton
And the roughness of dried, sticky toffee
And her coat was made.

For speed,
She used the owl's silence,
But the swiftness of an eagle
And the speed of light.

For sight,
She used an owl's sharpness,
She stole a human's clearness
And an eagle's distance.

And Horse was made.

Kelly-Jade Browning (10)
Heathcoat Primary School, Tiverton

Rabbit

(Based on 'Cat Began' by Andrew Matthews)

She took the whiteness of the snow for the colour of her coat,
She took the softness from cotton wool to add to her coat,
She took the blue from the sky to make her eyes,
She took the springiness from springs to make her hop,
She took velvet to make her ears
And the rabbit was made.

Enya Gooding (10)
Heathcoat Primary School, Tiverton

The Sky

At night when I go to bed,
I like to watch the sky,
With my dad all of the time,
So my dad and I want to fly.

Now we wear sunscreen,
When we sit in our garden, we start to fry,
It's really cool and we rest all day,
So now we want to buy the sky.

Our aunt thinks we're crazy,
We still want to buy the sky and we don't know why,
She goes ballistic at us, she's bonkers
And we still love the sky.

Megan Scott (11)
Heathcoat Primary School, Tiverton

My Pet Monkey

My pet monkey sits on my bed,
My pet monkey likes to wear red,
My pet monkey has spots on his legs,
My pet monkey's name is Greg.

My pet monkey drives a car,
My pet monkey plays the guitar,
My pet monkey followed me to school,
My pet monkey fell in the pool.

My pet monkey rides a bike,
My pet monkey eats and writes,
My pet monkey has lots of lunch,
My pet monkey likes to munch.

Sophie Short (10)
Heathcoat Primary School, Tiverton

Chicken Began

(Based on 'Cat Began' by Andrew Matthews)

For his beak,
He stole the point of an arrow,
The curve of the moon
And the pointed end of the stars.

For his feet,
He stole the sharpness of a pin,
The point of a prickle
And the long, rough bark from a tree.

For his neck,
He stole a lamp post,
For the length of his neck
And the fur off a carpet.

And Chicken was made!

Brandon Houldsworth (11)
Heathcoat Primary School, Tiverton

Dog Began

(Based on 'Cat Began' by Andrew Matthews)

I stole my howl from the wind,
I stole my coat from a fluffy carpet,
I stole my claws from a sickle,
I stole my eyes from the stars.

I stole my tail from a snake,
I stole my ears from a rabbit,
I stole my nose from the wet grass,
I stole my run from a cheetah.

Josh Ward (11)
Heathcoat Primary School, Tiverton

Horse

(Based on 'Cat Began' by Andrew Matthews)

He stole the darkness out of the mud,
He took the softness of the grass,
He stole the blue sky for his eyes,
He took the silver out of the moon.

He stole the goldness out of the sun,
He took the tree stumps for his legs,
He stole the clouds' shape for his face,
He took the leaves' shape for his ears.

He stole the donut rings for his nose,
He took the whiteness off the snow for his teeth,
He took the short tree's stump for his neck,
He stole the shortness of a bear for his body.

Then horses were made.

Zoe Dickinson (10)
Heathcoat Primary School, Tiverton

Midnight Wolf

The wolf came in the middle of the night,
Eyes gleaming, what a sight!

Ears pointed in the beaming sky.

Now the silky fur glistens in day
And through the moonlight.

Leaping down rock by rock.

Killing creatures, what a shock!

This is how the wolf plays
And this is how the wolf
Rules the day!

Lewis Hibbert (11)
Heathcoat Primary School, Tiverton

The Creation Of The Snake

Based on 'Cat Began' by Andrew Matthews)

Snake began
She took the darkness of the pool
For its eyes.

She took the sharpness of a farmer's pitchfork,
To make her eyes,
She took a painting out the painting shop for its patterns.

She took the dinosaur's tooth,
For its fangs
And took a snail's shell
For its coily
Tail
Snake
Began.

Hal Kingston (11)
Heathcoat Primary School, Tiverton

Fox

It took the bullet of a gun,
It took chasing of dogs.

The deepness of the night made its eyes,
The sharpness of the wind made its claws,
The orange of the fur shone to the moon.

Its tail like a snake's body
And its ears pointed as a beak,
Its teeth ready to snap!

And that's the night it went hunting.

Shannon Collins (10)
Heathcoat Primary School, Tiverton

My Garden Gnome

My garden gnome is rather short,
He is the most peculiar sort,
He has a large pointy nose,
Which nearly touches his hairy toes.

My garden gnome guards the house,
He is as quiet as a mouse,
He stands as still as a stone
And never lets out a single moan.

His cheeks are a rosy red,
He never ever goes to bed,
He guards the house rather well,
All in all, he's just swell.

Ethan Billing (10)
Heathcoat Primary School, Tiverton

Wolf Began

Based on 'Cat Began' by Andrew Matthews)

The wolf stole the darkness,
From the night sky,
To make the darkness,
For his coat.

Then he took the howl from the wind,
Now the worst thing of all,
He stole,
Blades for his claws.

Alex Snell (11)
Heathcoat Primary School, Tiverton

Lion Began

(Based on 'Cat Began' by Andrew Matthews)

Lion began
He took the sharpness of the rocks,
He borrowed the rumble of the thunder,
That made his voice.

For his stride,
He took the walk of a king,
He borrowed the pounce of a spring,
That made his stride.

For his eyes,
He took the brightness of headlamps,
He borrowed the scanning of a radar.

That made his eyes.

Ben Beaver (10)
Heathcoat Primary School, Tiverton

What Am I?

I live on the mountain tops,
Deep in the snow,
Eating everything in my path,
I am a carnivore,
I have black and white spots,
What am I?

A: I am a snow leopard.

Adam Bennett (11)
Heathcoat Primary School, Tiverton

The Cheetah Ran

Based on 'Cat Began' by Andrew Matthews)

She took the softness from cotton wool,
She added carpet
And the pattern from a painting,
To make the dotty fur.

She took the shining moon
And the blackness of a dark night,
She added the blue from the sky,
To make the shining eyes and the black nose.

She took the fastness from a shooting star,
She took the smoothness of the calm sea,
She added the balance from a trapeze artist
And the cheetah ran.

Jasmin Summers (11)
Heathcoat Primary School, Tiverton

The Bat Flew

T he eyes he stole from the sun,
H is stealth he took from the night,
E ars he swept from the birds at dawn.

B orrowing from the trees, his legs,
A nd from the velvet sky, his fur,
T aking from the mountains, his teeth.

F eelings he stripped from the deer,
L ying to the gullible creature,
E yeing the beauty of the cows' leather,
W ings were made for him.

And the bat flew.

Taran Stevenson (11)
Heathcoat Primary School, Tiverton

My Pet Cat

My pet cat lies on my bed,
My pet cat is called Greg,
My pet cat has a broken leg,
My pet cat hates the name Greg.

My pet cat eats lots of fish,
My pet cat has a big fat dish,
My pet cat likes to play,
My pet cat hates the colour grey.

My pet cat rides different bikes,
My pet cat eats and writes,
My pet cat has lots of friends,
My pet cat twists and bends.

Katie Hales (11)
Heathcoat Primary School, Tiverton

Snake Began

He took the rustle of the trees,
He took the movement of the grass,
He took the Y from the alphabet.

He took the tail of a cat,
He took the silkiness of a fish,
The fangs he took were from a wolf.

The thing he made was a snake,
With fangs from wolves,
Skin from fish
And the tail of a cat.

Louise Nash (11)
Heathcoat Primary School, Tiverton

Gorilla

The darkness of the night,
The blackness of the deep,
The shadows of a mountain
And the ash of a fire,
For its black fur.

The weight of a car,
The hardness of a rock,
The squareness of a cube
And the warmth of the sun,
For its beautiful body.

The shine of the moon,
The light of the stars,
The reflection of the planets
And the darkness of the universe,
For its shiny eyes.

The power of lightning,
The weight of a bear,
The speed of an eagle
And the strength of a lion,
For itself.

Joseph Zilch (11)
Heathcoat Primary School, Tiverton

My Pet Mummy

My pet mummy
Is really quite dumb,
When he tries to haunt me,
He falls on his bum.

I found him in a pyramid all on his own,
All he is is skin and bone,
He has a girlfriend whose name is Joan,
She is also just skin and bone.

He sleeps in a tomb,
In his own bedroom,
I wonder whom,
He was - maybe Tutankhamen.

He writes on papyrus,
With his own mummy pen,
He sleeps with his little fat hen,
He plays with plastic army men.

He keeps all his
Canopic jars lined in a row,
When it comes to morning,
His little hen crows.

Tilly Oxenham Babb (10)
Heathcoat Primary School, Tiverton

Untitled

The eagle took the swiftness from the swift
And the speed from a falcon.

It took the baldness from the baldest lion,
It took its claws from the cheetah.

For its wings, it took the bat's wings.

For its beak it took the sharpness from the penknife.

For its eyes, it stole the eyes from the owl of the night.

Aaron Young (11)
Heathcoat Primary School, Tiverton

When I Grow Up

One day I asked my brother,
'What's the point in growing up?'
He said, 'Don't be so stupid,
When you grow up, you could be . . .

Big, strong, fearless, boss of the world.

For this bro is a miracle.'

'Mum what's the point in growing up?
It's as boring as watching paint dry.'
She said, 'Don't be stupid, when you grow up you could be . . .

Famous, important, special, friendly, kind,
But especially you could be perfect.'

'Dad could you tell me the point
In growing up?'
He said, 'Don't be so silly lad, when you grow up you could be . . .

Speedy, fast, supersonic,
But especially you could be like me.'

Lloyd Marren (9)
Keyham Barton RC Primary School, Keyham

The Wind In Rome

I pulled up some ice cream and made it spin in the air,
I spread the sound cheering languages across St Peter's Square,
I scooped up a handful of water from the
Trevey Fountain and threw it onto the Coliseum,
Where they battled against big cats.
I lifted up a pizza and threw it at a man,
I knocked a map from a tourist's hands,
I hurried through the Mondale Hotel,
As I was going into town,
I became tired, exhausted and sleepy
And I needed to have a lie down.

Simon Sowden (9)
Keyham Barton RC Primary School, Keyham

Winter

Take some sprinkled cold snowballs,
Some gloves, coat and scarf,
To make a big snowball fight,
Add some cold raindrops,
Some breezy winds
And cold, snowy feet.

Mix with hot flaming fires,
Some hailstones drifting from the air
And peaceful, loving children,
Fetch a big tall tree,
Decorated with some lights
And a shining star on the top.

Leave some snow in your freezer,
For three whole months
And you have made winter.

Naomi Hitchcock (9)
Keyham Barton RC Primary School, Keyham

Lament Of A Chernobyl Child

Once I lay in a cot
And stared at the ceiling,
I heard children crying
And wheelchairs wheeling.

Now I'm not alone,
Carers are here,
They put the alphabet next to me,
I taught myself the ABC.

Sometimes I go to discos,
Vova pushes me around
To the music
And to the sound.

I went to a holiday camp,
We had lots of fun,
Lying around in the sun.

I then went to boarding school
And learnt lots of things,
I wore make-up
And acted really cool.

I love boarding school
And all of the rules,
Having fun all the time,
That's why I
Made this rhyme.

I hope you've enjoyed the end,
As all my love and hope shall send.

Holly May Clemens (9)
Keyham Barton RC Primary School, Keyham

Growing Up

When I grow up
I want to be . . .
Attractive,
Gorgeous, glamorous, glorious,
Sweet and cute,
But exquisite.

When I grow up
I want to be . . .
Clear,
Gleaming, glistening, glittering,
Dazzling and cheerful,
Also colourful.

When I grow up
I want to be . . .
Interesting,
Entertaining, amusing, exciting,
Remarkable and amazing,
But also thrilling.

When I grow up I don't want to be . . .
Evil!

Jade Crotty (9)
Keyham Barton RC Primary School, Keyham

Lament Of A Chernobyl Child

Once I lay in a cot
And stared at the ceiling,
I heard children crying
And sometimes I do too.

Now there is no more cot,
The visitors have come to me,
I always talk to them
And they talk back to me.

They put me in a wheelchair
And wheeled me into the garden,
I smelt the flowers
And heard the birds sing sweet songs.

Today I will go to a boarding school
And learn some new things,
If they ask me question,
I will only say yes or no.

Kayleigh Ward (9)
Keyham Barton RC Primary School, Keyham

Johnathon Banks

(Based on lyrics from 'Eleanor Rigby' by John Lennon and Paul McCartney)

Ah, look at all the homeless people!
Ah, look at all the homeless people!

Johnathon Banks,
Lives in a cardboard box which someone threw out,
Without a doubt,
Waits in the rain,
For someone to give him a tip,
So he can get a sip,
What is the point?

All the homeless people,
Where do they all come from?
All the homeless people,
Where do they all belong?

William Johnson,
Struggles to eat at night,
Holds on with might,
Looks at a house,
What is the point of his life?
Cuts his throat with a knife.

Ah, look at all the homeless people!
Ah, look at all the homeless people!

William Johnson,
Died on the street in despair,
What did he care?
Johnathon Banks,
Walks past the scene that makes him sad,
No one is glad.

All the homeless people,
Where do they all come from?
All the homeless people,
Where do they all belong?

Sam Thompson (11)
Lostwithiel School, Lostwithiel

Derek Valentine

(Based on lyrics from 'Eleanor Rigby' by John Lennon and Paul McCartney)

Ah, look at all the loveless people!
Ah, look at all the loveless people!

Derek Valentine,
Picks up the petals that have fallen,
From the roses,
Lives for his love,
Waits at the window,
Saving his heart to treasure with
Someone special,
Who will it be?

All the loveless people,
Who do they long for?
All the loveless people,
With who do they belong?

Angelica Baker,
Slaps on her make-up and puts on a smile,
That no one will see,
What do they care?
Look at her hoping,
For her wonderful dreams to come true,
But there's no one to love,
Have they all hearts of stone?

All the loveless people,
Who do they all long for?
All the loveless people,
With who do they belong?

Ah, look at all the loveless people!
Ah, look at all the loveless people!

Derek Valentine,
Jumped off a five storey building,
With no one to love,
Heaven's above,
Angelica Baker,
Laid flowers by his lonely grave to
Show that she cared,
If only they'd met.

All the loveless people,
Who do they all long for?
All the loveless people,
With who do they belong?

Megan Erwin & Rebecca Mortiboy (11)
Lostwithiel School, Lostwithiel

Billy Goston

(Based on lyrics from 'Eleanor Rigby' by John Lennon and Paul McCartney)

Ah, look at all the homeless people!
Ah, look at all the homeless people!

Billy Goston,
Feeding the ducks with all of his bread,
On a park bench,
With hands in his pockets,
On the footpath with his head bowed down to the ground,
Why is he there?

All the homeless people, where do they all come from?
All the homeless people, where do they all belong?

Mr McDoorsie,
Plants the flowers as some people go by,
Which no one will care for,
Packing away,
He puts his shovel and trowel in the shed,
Why does he do it?

All the homeless people, where do they all belong?
All the homeless people, where do they all come from?

Maxwell Davidson (10)
Lostwithiel School, Lostwithiel

Johnathon Davids

(Based on lyrics from 'Eleanor Rigby' by John Lennon and Paul McCartney)

Johnathon Davids,
Buying a suit from the tailor that nobody knows,
Nobody goes,
Drives back from town,
Treating his family like they should be wearing a crown,
What do they care?

All the rich people,
Where is their money from?
All the rich people,
Where do they all come from?

Johnathon's brother,
Lives in the house that he won in the sun,
Has lots of fun,
Look at him playing,
With both his children, his wife and his pet,
He'll never forget.

All the rich people,
Where is their money from?
All the rich people,
Where do they all come from?

Johnathon Davids,
Died in his house and was buried along with his wealth,
All by himself,
Johnathon's brother,
Kneeling and weeping all over the marble gravestone,
Standing alone.

All the rich people,
Where is their money from?
All the rich people,
Where do they all belong?

Piran Phippen & Jack Davidge (10)
Lostwithiel School, Lostwithiel

Lofty Cartwheel

(Based on lyrics from 'Eleanor Rigby' by John Lennon and Paul McCartney)

Ah, look at all the homeless people!
Ah, look at all the homeless people!

Lofty Cartwheel,
Playing his Game Boy while
Scoffing burgers,
Sits in a dream,
Looks out his window,
Waiting for friends to pass his door,
Where are they from?

Mother Mcally,
Cooking bacon and chips while
No one is there,
Look at them starving,
Cooking marshmallows with a stick,
That's what they do.

Lofty Cartwheel,
Died with brain damage in his homeland,
Mum and Dad came,
Mother Mcally,
Wiping the mud from her hands as the left the grave,
No one was there now.

All the homeless people,
Where did they come from?
All the homeless people,
Where do they belong?

Jordan Cummings (10)
Lostwithiel School, Lostwithiel

Famous People

(Based on lyrics from 'Eleanor Rigby' by John Lennon and Paul McCartney)

Eliyah Jackson,
Reading the timetable,
Whilst on the commuter train,
Standing in a cage of lions,
Staring out the window,
Reflection of his shadow,
What is it for?

All the famous people,
Where do they all come from?
All the famous people,
Where do they all belong?

Johnathon Jackson,
Doing the high jump,
One will die,
No one comes near,
Look at him dying,
Oh my dad is dead,
There's nobody there,
What do they care?

All the famous people,
Where do they all come from?
All the famous people,
Where do they all belong?

Johnathon Jackson,
Fell off a building and died,
With his name he was buried,
A long time ago,
How do you know?

All the famous people,
Where do they all come from?
All the famous people,
Where do they all belong?

Jacob Rickard (10)
Lostwithiel School, Lostwithiel

Jessica Cookie

(Based on lyrics from 'Eleanor Rigby' by John Lennon and Paul McCartney)

Ah, look at all the sad, sad people!
Ah, look at all the sad, sad people!

Jessica Cookie,
Sits in her garden with absolute silence,
Living and dreaming with nothing to do,
Wearing a face that is stained with salt tears,
Never a sound,
Why is this so?

All the sad, sad people!
Where do they all come from?
All the sad, sad people,
Where do they all belong?

Mother McKenzie,
Writing the words of praise for the Lord,
That she loves,
No one will know,
Look at her working,
Throughout the light of night and day,
When nobody's there,
What does she care?

All the sad, sad people,
Where do they all come from?
All the sad, sad people,
Where do they all belong?

Ah, look at all the sad, sad people!
Ah, look at all the sad, sad people!

Jessica Cookie,
Jumped in a fire and turned to black ashes,
Nobody came,
Mother McKenzie,
Sprinkling the dirt from the put out fire,
As she walks from the coal,
No one was saved.

Meghan Prindl (10)
Lostwithiel School, Lostwithiel

Kyle McKenzie

(Based on lyrics from 'Eleanor Rigby' by John Lennon and Paul McCartney)

Ah, look at all the boring people!
Ah, think about all the boring people!

Kyle McKenzie,
Picks up the keys in the drawer,
Where a slug has been,
Lives in a dream waiting at
The door wearing the glasses
That he keeps in a pocket
By the seat, where is the radio?

All the boring people,
Where do they all come from?
All the boring people,
Where do they all come from?

Kyle McKenzie,
Starting the car of a camper van,
That people will hear, no one comes near,
Look at him driving his camper in the morning,
When there's nobody there,
But does he care?

Ah, look at the boring people!
Ah, think of the boring people!

Kyle McKenzie,
Died in the car and was buried along with his name,
Nobody cared - John McKenzie brushing the dirt from his hands,
As he creeps from the graveyard,
Nobody cares.

All the boring people,
Where do they all come from?
All the boring people,
Where do they all come from?

Michael Sweet (10)
Lostwithiel School, Lostwithiel

Isabel Baker

(Based on lyrics from 'Eleanor Rigby' by John Lennon and Paul McCartney)

Ah, look at all the jealous people,
Ah, look at all the jealous people.

Isabel Baker,
Stands in the street watching people walk past,
Looks in a dream,
Looking at clothing wishing she had lots of money,
To buy all these things,
Where does it come from?

All the jealous people,
Where do they all come from?
All the jealous people,
Where do they all belong?

Shopkeeper Wendy,
Closing the shops so that people don't steal,
Why do they bother?
As the night falls poor Wendy is cleaning the
Counters from dirt,
What does she care?

All the jealous people,
Where do they all come from?
All the jealous people,
Where do they all belong?

Isabel Baker,
Died on the street of pneumonia,
Nobody noticed,
Shopkeeper Wendy,
Crying of shock as the time passed by,
No one was saved.

All the jealous people,
Where do they all come from?
All the jealous people,
Where do they all belong?

Amy Dunlap (11)
Lostwithiel School, Lostwithiel

Busy People

(Based on lyrics from 'Eleanor Rigby' by John Lennon and Paul McCartney)

Ah, look at all the busy people!
Ah, look at all the busy people!

Jonathon Smith,
Wakes up early to catch the train in the morning,
Waiting and yawning,
For the train to grind to a halt,
Lives in business,
Tucked up in an office answering phones,
Can't anyone moan?

All the busy people,
Where do they all come from?
All the busy people,
Where do they all belong?

James Enlect,
Counting the profits that
Make up his life,
Laughs with might,
When Jonathon comes home,
Yes his wife can moan.

All the busy people,
Where do they all come from?
All the busy people,
Where do they all belong?

Ah, look at all the busy people!
Ah, look at all the busy people!

Father Michael,
Looks sadly at a family,
That once had a man,
Can't everyone moan?

Thomas Mileham (11)
Lostwithiel School, Lostwithiel

Cheerful People

(Based on lyrics from 'Eleanor Rigby' by John Lennon and Paul McCartney)

Michael McKenzie,
Smiles at anyone he sees on a jolly morning,
There is no warning,
Visiting a friend,
At number 15 Jolly Street,
You would like to meet.

All the cheerful people,
Where do they all come from?
All the cheerful people,
Where do they all belong?

Lennon Jackson,
Trying to smile to cheer other people up,
Give him the thumbs up,
Look he is successful,
Even the dogs are smiling at him,
They're not too thin.

All the cheerful people,
Where do they all come from?
All the cheerful people,
Where do they all come from?

Ah, look at all the cheerful people,
Ah, look at all the cheerful people.

Michael McKenzie,
Visiting the place at number 15 Jolly Street,
All of a sudden,
Lennon Jackson walks around the corner to Jolly Street
And returns home smiling.

Ah, look at all the cheerful people,
Ah, look at all the cheerful people.

Simon Trebilcock (10)
Lostwithiel School, Lostwithiel

Isabel Clarkson

(Based on lyrics from 'Eleanor Rigby' by John Lennon and Paul McCartney)

Ah, look at all the tired people!
Ah, look at all the tired people!

Isabel Clarkson,
While getting her breakfast she sits in a chair yawning,
Sleeps in a dream,
Waits for her coffee,
While wearing her pyjamas, she eats up her breakfast,
Who is it for?

All the tired people,
Where do they come from?
All the tired people,
Where do they all belong?

Robert Pedersen,
Who is laying in bed with his wife not getting up,
Who dreams of his kids
And his dreams come true,
Never early for work,
He wakes up at night and gets a drink
And goes back to bed,
What is it for?

All the tired people,
Where do they all come from?
All the tired people,
Where do they all belong?

Ah, look at all the tired people!
Ah, look at all the tired people!

Isabel Clarkson,
Died in the woods where there was no food, no water,
Nobody to care for,
Nobody saw her,
Robert Pedersen,
Who went for a jog and got a job and felt much better,
Someone was saved.

Gabrielle Pedersen (11)
Lostwithiel School, Lostwithiel

Jessica Parker

(Based on lyrics from 'Eleanor Rigby' by John Lennon and Paul McCartney)

Ah, look at all the famous people,
Ah, look at all the famous people.

Jessica Parker,
Reading a magazine looks at lies being told,
Lives in a scene,
Waits in the studio,
Looking at clothes she is made to wear,
Why is she there?

All the famous people,
Where do they all come from?
All the famous people,
Where do they all belong?

Joseph Frank,
Taking pictures of famous people going by,
Lives in a dream,
Watching the leaves falling,
Down from the trees,
What is he doing?

All the famous people,
Where do they all come from?
All the famous people,
Where do they all belong?

Jessica Parker,
Looks in the mirror and thinks
What have I done?
She is not there anymore only
A made-up figure.

Joseph Frank,
Lies in a hospital bed,
He's nearly dead,
Because of the lies and deceit that were told.

Rhyanah Kingston (10)
Lostwithiel School, Lostwithiel

Look At All The Busy People

(Based on lyrics from 'Eleanor Rigby' by John Lennon and Paul McCartney)

Ah, look at the busy people,
Ah, look at the busy people.

Mark Johnson,
Writing all his important work,
Wondering into a dream,
Staring out of the window,
Wishing he was a billionaire.

All the busy people,
When will they ever get along?
All the busy people,
Where do they all belong?

Father McWesly,
Miming the song that nobody will hear,
You would not dare go near,
Watch him at work,
Nobody's there,
He does not care.

All the busy people,
When will they get along?
All the busy people,
Where do they all belong?

Ah, look at all the busy people.

Mark Johnson,
Laid to rest on the coffin bed, he was buried,
With his name,
No one cared,
Father McWesly
Brushing the dirt off his hands,
Limps from the gravestone,
No one was spared.

Johnathon Barnes (11)
Lostwithiel School, Lostwithiel

A Poem Based On Mark Johnson
And Michael Stuwart

(Based on lyrics from 'Eleanor Rigby' by John Lennon and Paul McCartney)

Ah, look at all the selfish people!
Ah, look at all the selfish people!

Mark Johnson and Michael Stuwart,
On the computer next to each other,
In their dreams, staring out of the computer,
Screen not commuting with each other,
Turning the screens to the side,
So they will not copy,
This is called selfish people.

All the selfish people,
Where do they all come from?
All the selfish people,
Where do they all belong?

Mark Johnson,
Typing notes that no one will hear,
With no one there,
Look at him typing,
Typing overnight, working so hard.
What does he care?

All the selfish people,
Where do they all come from?
All the selfish people,
Where do they all belong?

Ah, look at all the selfish people!
Ah, look at all the selfish people!

All the selfish people,
Where do they all come from?
All the selfish people,
Where do they all belong?

Kyle Chapman (11)
Lostwithiel School, Lostwithiel

Katherine Spindle

(Based on lyrics from 'Eleanor Rigby' by John Lennon and Paul McCartney)

Ah, look at all the mournful people!
Ah, look at all the mournful people!

Katherine Spindle,
Sniffs into her tissue she's used,
Many times before,
Lives in the mist,
Waits at the postbox,
Wearing the face glazed with tears she believes
Will relive the pain,
Who is it for?

Henry McFrenzie,
Writing the words of a letter that no one will read,
Just out of creed,
Look at him writing,
Licking the stamp and address in the night,
When light isn't there,
What does he care?

All the mournful people,
Where do they all come from?
All the mournful people,
Where do they all belong?

Ah, look at all the mournful people!
Ah, look at all the mournful people!

Katherine Spindle,
Died in the park with autumn leaves,
As red as her heart,
Surrounded by blood,
Henry McFrenzie,
Sets down the letter he wrote for his love,
Down on the grave,
No one was saved.

All the mournful people,
Where do they all come from?
All the mournful people,
Where do they all belong?

Grace Edward-Collins (11)
Lostwithiel School, Lostwithiel

Storm

As I look out onto sea,
I wonder what it'd be like to be,
In the eye of the storm.

The writhing sea,
The crashing waves,
That's the way the sea behaves,
But I'm in my house, all safe and sound,
As the storm scrapes at my window,
Like a baying hound.

Nessa Whitworth (11)
Mithian School, St Agnes

Jealousy

Jealousy is an evil cloud,
That lurks in your head
And never comes out,
It only goes away when you're in bed.

Jealousy is a dying feeling,
That only comes out when you are needing,
You cannot see it, you cannot taste it,
You can only feel it.

Jealousy can kill,
Jealousy can steal,
Jealousy can make you kneel,
Before its mighty power.

Ben Green (11)
Mithian School, St Agnes

Relief

Relief is a sigh of hope,
A blooming flower stretching to the sky,
Reaching up from the stumble,
Now feeling tremendously high,
The pain has stopped
And all you're doing is going up, up high,
The tables are turning,
It's stopped all the churning,
I feel like shouting to the world,
Relief, relief,
I am finally cured.

Brittany Snook (11)
Mithian School, St Agnes

Happiness

Happiness is a bright blue flower,
Bursting into the sunlight,
Happiness is a waterfall,
Thumping down in the sun.

Happiness is good friends,
Cheering you up when you're down,
Happiness is spring,
New chicks and birds being born.

Happiness is a kitten being born,
With its cute, furless face and body,
Happiness is Christmas presents under the tree,
With the fairy on the top and tunes on the piano.

Serena Jones (10)
Mithian School, St Agnes

Fear

Fear is a dark cloud,
The owl hooting in the dark,
A fear of dying at any moment,
Fear is when you stand up to a bully,
Fear is when you forget your homework.

Fear is when you pull a trigger,
Fear is a torture,
Fear is the unknown,
Fear is the worst feeling.

Josh Job (10)
Mithian School, St Agnes

Tigers

Tigers lurking in the shade,
Tigers growling in a parade,
Tigers never lose their stripes,
Always ready for a fight.

Tigers are silent killers,
Tigers' meals are real fillers,
Tigers are the spillers of blood,
Tigers never roll in mud.

Harry Waters (11)
Mithian School, St Agnes

Anger Is . . .

Anger is a torment,
A curse,
A pain that stays,
You become someone else.

Steam emerges from your head,
You have a rage that never goes away,
Anger is powerful - don't underestimate it.

Matt Wood (10)
Mithian School, St Agnes

September

September is a brown cloak,
Crisp and crackling under my feet,
Animals making nests,
For winter,
Trees dropping their leaves,
Leaving a soft carpet,
People harvesting crops,
Happy and safe for winter.

Isabel Evans (10)
Mithian School, St Agnes

Frustration

Frustration is a spinning top,
Swirling in your head,
A brain-busting knife,
Digging into your brain.

Frustration is a crazy car,
Speeding around your head,
A long run after dinner,
Making you ill.

Frustration is double maths,
On a Monday morning,
Frustration is SATs,
Frustration is choosing a new pet,
When there's loads and loads.

Olivia Richardson (10)
Mithian School, St Agnes

Spiders In The Classroom

Spider in the classroom,
Spider in the dustbin,
Spider in the toilet,
Spider in the bath,
Spider in your tap,
Spider on your mat,
Spider on your hat,
Spider on your cat,
There's a spider on your bed,
Where is that spider *now*?

Kirsty Robertson (8)
Nanstallon Community Primary School, Bodmin

There's A Rumble In The Jungle

There's a rumble in the jungle,
Where nobody goes, there's a great big elephant,
Blowing his nose, with a doogy, boogy, wooby, wooby,
Woody, down in the jungle where nobody goes.

There's a rumble in the jungle,
Where nobody goes,
There's a big tiger painting his toes,
With a doogy, boogy, wooby, wooby,
Woody down in the jungle, where nobody goes.

There's a rumble in the jungle,
Where nobody goes,
There's a great big hippo washing his clothes
With a doogy, boogy, wooby, wooby,
Woody down in the jungle where nobody goes!

Zenna Thorne (9)
Nanstallon Community Primary School, Bodmin

An Animal Day

The zebra came for breakfast,
The crocodile came from Texas,
The elephant came to play,
The hippo came to stay,
The lion came for lunch,
The monkey came for brunch,
The leopard came to see me,
The cheetah came for tea,
I hope he won't eat me!
The giraffe came for bed
And we both cuddled our ted.

Lydia Kate Hamley (9)
Nanstallon Community Primary School, Bodmin

Waves

The storm is coming, the waves are humming,
The blossom is turning red,
The seaweed is growing,
The rivers are flowing,
The time will wash the seabed,
The waves are like a thistle,
The wind will rustle and whistle,
The very hot sun will try to have some fun,
The sea is like a crystal,
It's like a water pistol
And when the sun sets in Devon,
It's like a gold star in Heaven.

Rhianna Louise Parkins (9)
Nanstallon Community Primary School, Bodmin

There's A Dragon . . .

There's a dragon in the car
And he's wearing a bra.

There's a dragon on the bus
And he's making a fuss.

There's a dragon on the street,
On a metal seat.

There's a dragon on the train,
Being a pain.

There's a dragon in an aircraft
And he's having a laugh.

There's a dragon in the house
And he's scared of a mouse.

Joel Corbett (8)
Nanstallon Community Primary School, Bodmin

When The Elephant Came For Tea

When the elephant came for breakfast,
We had cheese on toast.

When the elephant came for dinner,
We had a cup of tea and a handful of peas.

When the elephant came for tea,
He made funny faces at me!

And that's the day the elephant came for tea.

Lucy Drew (9)
Nanstallon Community Primary School, Bodmin

Animals

The hippo came for lunch,
The monkey with a bunch,
The lion came to stay,
The zebra came to play,
The cheetah came in speed,
The dog came with a lead,
The leopard had a herd,
The panther didn't say a word.

Rosey Phillips (9)
Nanstallon Community Primary School, Bodmin

What?

Silvery, gloomy, white,
Catch me when I'm in sight,
You will only see me at night.

Streams reflect me,
Astronauts protect me,
What am I?
I'm the moon!

Rosie Ings (9)
Nanstallon Community Primary School, Bodmin

Dragons

Dragons, dragons, everywhere,
Read them in a book while sat in a chair,
If you go there, go with a knight,
Just in case, you get in a fight,
I stole some treasure from the den,
I saw the dragon, he's as fat as a hen.

He is in a cave,
He is so brave,
He's not hairy,
But he's so scary,
Oh no, he's woken up - argh!

Henry Ellis (8)
Nanstallon Community Primary School, Bodmin

Spider's Poem

Spider in the classroom,
Run! Run! Run!
Spider in the classroom,
Fun! Fun! Fun!
Spider in the classroom,
Scream! Scream! Scream!
Spider in the classroom,
Dream! Dream! Dream!

Amy Ellery (7)
Nanstallon Community Primary School, Bodmin

My Brother

My big brother is very smelly,
He smells of aftershave,
He likes to play with the girls,
But never does behave.

Mel Parkyn (9)
Nanstallon Community Primary School, Bodmin

There's An Elephant In My Head

There's an elephant in my head,
It's pink, blue and red,
It's lying in a bed
And it said,
'I'm little and I'm big,
I'm heavy and I'm light,
I have a hard, soft bite
And I sleep through the night!

Alice Smith (9)
Nanstallon Community Primary School, Bodmin

Love

Love is like roses in ice-cold water,
Love is like hearts ripped apart,
Love is like a babe being born,
Love is like somebody being saved,
Love is like eating a jam tart,
When I'm above
I'll still love.

Megan Ranger (8)
Nanstallon Community Primary School, Bodmin

Is The Moon Tired?

Is the moon tired? She looks so pale,
Within her misty veil,
She scares the sky from east to west
And takes no rest.

Before the coming of night,
The moon shines papery white,
Before the dawning of the day,
She fades away.

Shirley Anne Young (8)
Nanstallon Community Primary School, Bodmin

The Day The Zebra Came For Tea

The day the zebra came for tea,
He turned up unexpectedly.

He ate up all the wobbly jelly,
Then he watched the boring telly!

Then he ate the jam Swiss roll
And in the chair he made a hole.

Then he ate the chocolate cake
And didn't go home till half-past eight!

Now it's time to tidy up,
Look he's used my favourite cup!

Sara Ellery (7)
Nanstallon Community Primary School, Bodmin

Untitled

There was a little girl of Pencoys,
Who liked to make lots of noise,
She made a big bang
And a small twang,
Then attracted all of the boys.

Lauren Strickland (8)
Pencoys Primary School, Redruth

Four Lanes - A Limerick

There was a young baby in Fourlanes,
Who had a very fast brain,
She talked all the time in song
And in rhyme
And never went outside again.

Rebecca Wood (8)
Pencoys Primary School, Redruth

What Am I?

Meat eater,
Cold-blooded
Hunter,
Super pouncer,
Fast runner,
Silent pounder,
Ambush expert.

A: A leopard!

Mathew Williams & Christopher King (8)
Pencoys Primary School, Redruth

What Am I?

Mouth washer,
Splash causer,
Eye stinger,
Wave producer,
Current carrier,
Roams around the world.

A: The sea.

Martha Carlisle (7)
Pencoys Primary School, Redruth

What Am I?

Orange growler,
Fast runner,
Meat eater,
Stripes striker,
Jungle survivor,
Sharp teeth.

A: A tiger.

Thomas Walsh & Towan Nicholas (7)
Pencoys Primary School, Redruth

What Am I?

Food nibbler,
Nut liker,
Small muncher,
Big hearer,
Cat hater,
Huge sleeper,
Watch out for the army.

A: Mouse.

Sarah Averiss (8)
Pencoys Primary School, Redruth

Redruth

There was a thin child from Redruth,
Who never told the truth,
He lied to his dad,
Who got very mad
And sent him up on the roof.

Shani Coxwell (8)
Pencoys Primary School, Redruth

What Am I?

Heat helper,
Energy provider,
Plant grower,
High floater,
Glad helper,
Light maker,
Colour changer,
Skin burner,
I collect energy.

A: The sun.

Tahlie Sharpe & Heather Sams
Pencoys Primary School, Redruth

What Am I?

Honey maker,
Stripy flyer,
Bizzy buzzer,
Hive liver,
Brilliant stinger,
Flower hopper,
Pollen . . . ater,
Beware of the queen
And her troops.

A: A bee.

**Natassja Gehr-Horrocks, Lauren Treseder
& Rhiannon Drew (8)**
Pencoys Primary School, Redruth

Dragon

Fire breather,
High flyer,
Big biter,
Big stealer,
Silent sleeper,
Loud snorer,
Big killer,
Scary monster,
Inferno fire.

Jake Fielder (7)
Pencoys Primary School, Redruth

My Limerick

There was a thin child from Redruth,
Whose horse only had one hoof,
It gave her a kick
And she felt very sick,
So she said something uncouth.

Chloe Pendrill (8)
Pencoys Primary School, Redruth

Animals

A nteaters eat ants in America,
N its nest nastily in hair,
I guanas live in India indulging insects,
M anattes are mammals that muddle in mild water,
A lligators eat ancient old men,
L eopards and lions live on the African plains,
S eals swim in the sea.

Thomas Woolf (10)
St Breward Primary School, Bodmin

Zany

Zany is purple like magnolia growing in my garden,
It tastes like crispy crackers,
It smells like ripe Stilton cheese,
It reminds me of the circus rushing
And tumbling over itself,
It feels like soft silk on your skin,
It sounds like a crazy butterfly buzzing in my brain.

Samantha Champion (10)
St Breward Primary School, Bodmin

Monster

M onster, monster edging closer,
O range teeth and orange tongue,
N asty nose,
S caly skull and snarling sneer,
T all as a terrific, terrifying tower.
E vil eyes and eyebrows,
R aucous rattling roar,

Lolita Diot Parslow (9)
St Breward Primary School, Bodmin

Happiness

Happiness is like a river,
Flowing down the street.

It sounds like birds singing,
Through the air.

It smells like love burning,
Through the air.

It reminds me of friendship.

It tastes like fresh air.

It reminds me of burning fire through the air.

Jack Kay (10)
St Breward Primary School, Bodmin

Feelings Inside

We all have special feelings inside,
Special feelings we shouldn't put aside,
Sometimes life can be a bumpy ride,
But here's one thing, 'Don't run and don't hide!'
We can be happy, scared and sometimes sad,
We can also be angry or a little bit mad,
But when your feelings get out of control,
Try not to be mean then you won't feel bad,
We all know bullies act big and strong,
But inside I bet they know bullying is wrong,
So that's one thing we've learnt here today,
If you stick up for yourself, bullies should stay away,
So if you have anything to do with violence,
Do not suffer in silence!

Emily Bunt (9)
St Breward Primary School, Bodmin

I Wish

I wish people would stop killing people,
I wish everybody was nice,
I wish everybody was not nasty or naughty,
I wish there were no terrible tsunamis,
I wish there were no earth-shattering earthquakes,
I wish the world was like this.

Joe Cornelius (10)
St Breward Primary School, Bodmin

Silence

Silence is white like fluffy clouds,
Silence tastes like fresh air from mountains,
Silence looks like a stream rushing by,
Silence feels like air rushing through your hands,
Silence smells like cut grass,
When I think of silence, I want to go to sleep,
Silence reminds me of relaxing.

Ryan Best (10)
St Breward Primary School, Bodmin

My Cat

My cat is lost
And I can't find her anywhere.

She's not in the tree,
She's not in the shed.

I was so sad,
I could hardly talk.

We searched everywhere,
But could not find her.

I found her in my bedroom,
I was so glad.

Marisa Nicholls (7)
St Mary's RC School, Falmouth

A Cornish Poem

It had been a long day,
Oh what can I say?
The smell was bad,
It made me scared and unbelievably sad.

The rocks came crumbling,
Down, down, down,
They were as sharp as a rich king's crown.

There was blood everywhere,
I was filled with fear,
I didn't know what to do,
I shed a tear.

To my surprise,
I heard a noise,
It was my father,
Some of the other boys.

They carried me quickly out the mine,
They dropped me over seven times,
My head was aching,
I could hear the banging of the tools.

I ate my pasty,
Which was smelling sweet,
All I could hear,
Was stamping feet.

A few weeks later,
I am at the mine,
Counting the days,
Counting the time.

Sadie Quinn (11) & Grace Morbey (10)
St Mary's RC School, Falmouth

Merry Maid Of Zennor

In Zennor there were two boys,
Zacky and Tommy, not many toys,
But friendly and good friends.

Church bells ting,
A golden ring,
The girl at the back of the church.

Seven weeks past,
The girl with the mask,
Stayed at the back of the church.

She ran away,
With Tommy one day
And they jumped into the sea.

The waterhole blew,
The water flew,
The seawater splashed Zacky's eyes.

A baby cry,
In the afternoon sky,
Tail of baby flipping in the grass.

Mother is here,
Without a fear,
Grabbing her baby she throws a golden shell.

Waves rise,
Anchor down,
The merry maid gave a frown.

'Move your anchor,
Move your anchor,
Move your anchor now.'

A secret from a merry maid,
A merry maid has already paid,
But the secret for you will have to wait
Till another day.

Laura Powell (10)
St Mary's RC School, Falmouth

Down In The Mine

Down in the mine,
A terrible time,
I was so full of fear,
I shed a tear.

Dust in my eyes,
Oh how I cried,
Rats gnawing at my feet,
Like I was fresh meat.

My dad is so bad,
I am so mad,
I smell blood, fear and sweat,
I am dirty like the man I just met.

Explosions everywhere,
But I'm too hungry to care,
The pasties make me feel a little better,
The damp walls are making me wetter.

I hear rumbling,
The walls are crumbling,
Quick, move out the way,
Don't stay!

A few more hours now,
How can I cope? How?
It has been a long day,
But I still have to stay.

Someone is falling,
They are screaming and calling,
A shudder is sent down my spine,
All because of this terrible mine.

I feel rather ill,
I can't stay still,
I don't want to come back tomorrow,
I am filled with sorrow.

Nearly time to go,
I feel so low,
It is a crime to be in a mine.

It is a crime to be in a mine!

Bethany Telling & Gemma Wallis (11)
St Mary's RC School, Falmouth

Down In The Mine

Down in the mine,
For such a long time,
Falling rocks,
Wearing no socks.

Children dying,
People crying,
So hardworking,
Feel like fainting.

Cold dark tunnels,
Small air funnels,
Hardly able to breathe,
Getting a disease.

Flickering lights,
People getting frights,
Noises everywhere,
People taking lots of care.

Down in the mine,
For such a long time.

Jessica McColl & Zoë Ferrier (10)
St Mary's RC School, Falmouth

The Miner's Poem

Bang, crash, thump, dead!
Miners die every day,
In the pain,
With the shame.

Nervous, unhappy, cold, upset,
Miners tapping,
At the walls,
Rocks fall down,
They give a frown.

Dust, gas, dampness, burning,
Hold on tight,
With all your might,
Flickering lights,
Insect bites.

Scared, lonely, explosion, blood,
Explosions appear,
Through the dust,
Miners die,
Before saying goodbye.

Warm, luxurious, tasty, tender,
Pasties are here,
For all to eat,
Dreaming while they eat,
With very smelly feet.

Home, warm, safe and sound,
Lucky to be home,
In one piece,
The day is now finished,
For another day.

Chloe Quick & Emily Quinn (11)
St Mary's RC School, Falmouth

The Underground Miner

As I climb through the mine,
I see my first thick tin line,
It's very dark and scary,
My boots 're getting 'eavy.

There's sweat dripping down me brow,
Father calls, 'Get 'ere now'
I climb down step by step,
But I'm not there yet.

'Ere I am at the bo'em,
Men all start work, there's a lot of 'em,
People start chiselling at the rock,
I think there's wa'er in me sock!

It's nearly lunch,
I feel like 'aving a munch,
I'll eat me pasty
And the crust - it's nasty.

Need to get to work,
Or they'll go berserk!
All this work, will drive me mad,
When we leave I'll be glad.

I am so very scared,
I wish some people cared,
For I heard the pixies knockin' (they're nasty)
I'm worried 'cause I didn't leave some of me pasty.

I can smell some burnin' gas,
I don't think I need to ask,
For I know the explosions will soon arrive,
Look for shelter, dive, dive, dive!

Lauren Turuelo, Lucinda Higginson (11) & Emma Snowden (10)
St Mary's RC School, Falmouth

A Day In The Mine

I am climbing down a ladder,
The smell is getting bad,
There are rats under my feet,
I just want to eat.

I am running through the mine,
I am checking on the time,
There are men clanging,
Explosions are banging.

I am eating my grub,
I have a very sore rib,
I feel sad,
I just want my dad.

I am climbing up the ladder,
I am getting less sad,
Because I can see the light
And it's getting more bright.

Zach Scrace & Lee Mitchell (11)
St Mary's RC School, Falmouth

Miner

Mining sounds fun,
Mining sounds good.

Mind the gas, it might be a close one,
Down below there is a lot of water,
Drill a hole,
The mine starts flooding.

Get out of the mine,
Quick! Quick! Quick!

Ben Stevenson (8)
St Mary's RC School, Falmouth

William Crago

Dark and deep,
There is no sleep,
In the flickering lights,
You see different sights.

In the mine,
You don't have much time,
In the deep,
You really weep.

I am so full of fear,
I shared a little tear,
Was so sad,
I wanted my dad.

I saw the beaming,
I heard screaming,
Of the light,
In the dark night.

I got out of the mine,
I saw a shine,
It was my mum,
She said, 'Welcome back chum.'

James Taylor & Kyren Coulls (11)
St Mary's RC School, Falmouth

Down The Mine

I'm climbing down the mine,
I don't know what to do,
I'm climbing down the ladder,
Oh no! I lost my shoe.

I see flickering faint lights,
Oh how I fear,
I'm getting really scared,
I'm going to shed at tear.

I feel damp, cold and hungry,
My hands are going numb,
I feel ever so lonely,
I really want my mum.

I hear rocks falling,
People dying,
Explosions and banging,
Children crying.

I'm eating my pasty,
It tastes so great,
I could eat it forever,
For this mine I hate.

Now it's back to work,
It's been a very long day,
I want to get out of here,
What more can I say!

I'm getting really hot now,
When can I get out?
I'm feeling such discomfort,
I want to scream and shout!

Now the day is over,
And I can go home,
Have a rest by the fire
And eat my chicken to the bone.

I'm getting out the mine now,
Such a long way to the top,
I'm really getting tired,
My leg's so numb, I think I have to hop!

Cara Kiszczuk & Charlie Welch (11)
St Mary's RC School, Falmouth

The Robot Gorilla In The Rainforest

I can see the jungle's life going on below,
As I fly right through the trees,
Oh I just love it when it gets to breakfast, lunch or tea
Because we get to munch on each other's fleas,
I'm the daddy robot gorilla and my bones creak,
Squeak, clap and cheer,
Just poor lion's throat when he tries to roar and fear.

I can hear my children banging their chests
Like good girls and boys,
I can hear my friend Samba the lion,
Roaring like he shouldn't be.

I can smell the big green trees flowing side to side,
I can smell my prey running, trying to hide
And oh! I love the lovely flowers' smell standing nearby,
I can smell the feast my wife is cooking -
Bamboo pie (yum-yum!)

I feel the wind blowing at my face as I fly through the jungle's trees,
I feel the trees brushing my day's mud off my metal skin,
Oh I just love the feel of food digesting in my tummy
As I sit in the sun,
I can still taste the fleas from my last feast,
I can taste the rain clouds on their way,
Ready to pour as God's spray.

Madeleine Steele (7)
St Mary's RC School, Falmouth

First Day In A Mine

When you are climbing down the ladder,
The pain is already starting to set on your shoulder,
You are very scared,
Feeling as if you have just been dared.

It is very damp,
The only way you can see is with your lamp,
You can hear the banging of the pickaxe and the hammer
And the explosions of gunpowder.

Workmen are coming out of explosions covered in smoke,
They are coughing and starting to choke!
You are nervous, sad and worried,
Thinking you are going to be buried.

You can also hear the gad tapping
And the miners yapping,
You watch the rats scurry by,
Sometimes hearing a workman cry.

Your pickaxe is dented
And your hammer needs to be mended,
As you leave you feel a sigh of relief,
But still thinking about the workmen beneath.

Daniel Templeton & Joshua Wilkes (11)
St Mary's RC School, Falmouth

A Day In The Mine

I was going down the ladder,
Getting colder and colder,
I had arms that were starting to weaken,
There I was in the darkness.

I heard the pick banging against the rock,
Then there was a cry of danger,
A bang of gunpowder exploded,
Then rocks came tumbling down the shaft.

It was dinnertime,
Everyone was hungry,
It was pasty, everyone's favourite,
Half was a meal, half was a dessert.

After our dinner, it was back to work,
It was long and tiring,
Trying to find the right rock,
It was then time to go back up to the surface,
I was so relieved.

Andrew Bastin (10) & Ben Richardson (11)
St Mary's RC School, Falmouth

The Mermaid Of Zennor

There once was a mermaid of Zennor,
Who met a handsome young fella,
She dragged him down to the sea,
So they could live in glee!
Two years later they were seen,
With seven children from 1 to 13,
It was nice to know they were free!
In the dead of night Zachy saw a sight,
Of a beautiful baby.

Maybe it was a young mermaid's child
And she was very mild!
When suddenly her mum came to her
And he knew instantly,
That it was the mermaid's baby!

One day an anchor was blocking her cove,
The merry maid got on her knees and pleaded,
Because her children hadn't been fed,
The anchor was moved, hooray!

Katie Weston (10)
St Mary's RC School, Falmouth

The Merry Maid Of Zennor

There once was a merry maid of Zennor,
Who met a sweet young fella,
He sang in the choir with lots of fire,
Tom Taskis was his name.

He ran away one day during the month of May,
That's what people say, until the end of the day.

One stormy night on top of a cliff,
Young Zachy stood in a bit of a miff,
The waterhole blew,
Something went boom,
In a few seconds more,
A merchild was on the floor.

Rosie Caveney & Amy Woodland (10)
St Mary's RC School, Falmouth

A Miner's Poem

Down in the mines where it's dark and damp,
A young boy named William, smelt like a tramp,
Young William was feeling very depressed,
Because his pasty was cold, and so was his vest,
He was so broken-hearted,
Because he had only just started,
To dig after his daily rest.

William Crago was very worried,
In case he was hit from a rock,
He was in a big hurry,
Just as the day was ending,
The man engine rod started bending, it broke with a crack
And a snick and a snack and William was sent flying,
Finally, as a young lad William felt extremely bad
And was ready for another horrifying day tomorrow.

Tom Lobban & Brogan Conlon (11)
St Mary's RC School, Falmouth

Mining

The men are miners,
They go underground,
Through tunnels,
Dark and scary.

Deep down,
Under monstrous rocks,
Green, grey, pink,
With axes and shovels.

Lights and helmets,
It is hard to breathe,
Hot and sweaty,
Mining men are strong men.

Sam Robinson (8)
St Mary's RC School, Falmouth

The Merry Maid Of Zennor

A veil of mysterious Cornish mist,
Hangs low,
Over the barren, brown landscape . . .
Hiding untold secrets long forgotten!
Surrounding precious treasures,
A raging blue explosion of the calling sea,
Down in the deadly dark depths,
Lurk lost and unfortunate, ghostly souls,
Often wandering the desolate cliffs,
I think of stories of my ancestor Tom,
Gazing, staring, pondering, what mystery lies there?
The mystery of Tom Taskis and his merry maid,
Between the white horses galloping in,
I glimpse a face, a smile, a hand, a wave!
The remains of a story long ago . . .
It began with the two choirboys Zachy and Tom,
At the all-singing church a merry maid,
The golden hair, the wavy gown, the shell-shaped bonnet,
And then a gleaming scaly tail as she stole Tom Taskis away,
A year to pass, a year of loss, the friendless Zachy Pender,
Searching, searching the high cliffs,
Zachy tonight is curious
And from the blowhole a baby is born,
A baby of Tom and the merry maid,
Zachy saved the baby and received a reward,
A reward of gold and silver from the mother of the sea,
So I stand here silently wondering,
Reliving the story of Tom Taskis and the merry maid of Zennor,
Where? What? How and why? These questions lost for eternity
Only, I alone, still see my ancestor.

James Dommett (10)
St Mary's RC School, Falmouth

Merry Maid Of Zennor

A veil of mysterious mist hangs low over a brown and
Barren Cornish landscape,
Hiding untold secrets - long forgotten,
Surrounding precious treasures,
A raging blue explosion of the calling sea,
Down in the deadly dark depths,
Lurk lost and unfortunate ghostly souls.

Often wandering desolate clifftops,
I think of stories of my ancestor - Tom,
Gazing, staring, pondering, what mystery lies there?

The mystery of Tom Taskis and his merry maid,
Between the white horses galloping in,
I glimpse, a face, a smile, a hand, a wave.

Then something unexpected happened,
The surface of the water scattered
And out of the water emerged,
The head of an old friend of mine.

Her hair twined around her,
Acting like slippery seaweed,
When I caught sight of a ship laying anchor
And the bonny merry maid pleaded for them to stop.

The sailors obeyed at once
And the merry maid was gone
But back soon once more she came
With a family of nine.

And a wonderful sight I saw,
There were ripples all around,
Balancing a merchild on his head,
Was my old ancestor Tom Taskis.

Isabel Steele (10)
St Mary's RC School, Falmouth

Merry Maid Of Zennor

A veil of mysterious Cornish mist hangs
Low over a brown and barren landscape,
Hiding untold secrets - long forgotten and
Surrounding precious treasures.

A raging blue explosion of the calling sea,
Down in the deadly dark depths lurk lost
And unfortunately ghostly souls,
Often wandering the desolate cliffs,
I think of stories of my ancestor - Tom,
Gazing, staring, pondering, what mystery lies there?

The mystery of Tom Taskis and his merry maid,
Between the white horses galloping in,
I glimpse a face, a smile, a hand, a wave of the merry maid.

Strange tales of merry maid searching for love,
Drawn to the land by song,
To the church of Zennor where stood Tom,
Side by side with Zachy, his friend,
Taunting, tempting, tantalising into the stormy depths,
Whispering to Zachy to not say a word.

Six months did pass with no sight of the man,
When a miracle was seen,
An infant so fair came up from the sea.

As if to see her beginnings, young Zachy caught the babe,
But suddenly it was whisked from his grasp and replaced by
A golden shell.

Three months did pass without a sight of the merry maid,
But one day Zachy did see in the cove,
Her speak with a captain of the sea,
Without delay he set sail and was moved on his way,
One last glimpse of Tom, Zachy had and then they were gone.

Zachy the maker of stories would tell this
To his family and beyond.

Luke Mansfield (10)
St Mary's RC School, Falmouth

Merry Maid Of Zennor

One sunny Sunday morning,
Just as the day was dawning,
Zachy Pender went down to church,
He was singing with his friend Tom and
His tummy gave a lurch.

For there sat a beautiful girl,
With a dress that shimmered with a swirl,
She went, not long after Tom,
Before the church rang ding-dong.

Zachy chased them down the unnamed stream,
That let off a misty steam,
With a finger to his lips, Tom dived into the small river,
From where we get our fish dinner.

There was a raging storm one year
And the mist, it would not clear,
Zachy climbed up to the cliffs,
It was so cold that he felt stiff,
The storm it flew,
The waterhole blew,
It blinded Zachy's eye,
As he heard a baby cry,
He threw the babe over
And caught a shell, luckier than a four leaf clover.

Lydia Hawkins (9)
St Mary's RC School, Falmouth

The Merry Maid Of Zennor

There once was a merry maid of Zennor,
Who loved a handsome young fella,
They lived under the sea, where he had to agree
To become a merman forever.

Zachy waited on the dock,
While the clock went tick-tock,
He didn't know why
But then he heard a little cry.

The anchor was in the way
And it was the wrong time of day,
'Move your anchor,' she cried,
So they complied
And set sail away.

The mother came out of the deep,
Her baby was fast asleep,
Zachy counted seven children,
Then they turned for a leap.

Zoe Underwood (9)
St Mary's RC School, Falmouth

The Lifeboat

'Help! Help! Help!'
I shouted, swimming in the sea,
'Help! Help! Help!'
I shouted. 'Please rescue me.'

Big and orange,
Crashing through each wave,
Speeding over the water,
Looking for me to save.

Alexandra Pinhay (8)
St Mary's RC School, Falmouth

Merry Maid Of Zennor

At the back of the church hall,
Sat a nice girl on a stall,
She had long golden hair
And her skin was so fair,
Tom looked at her skin,
So beautiful and thin,
Seven weeks later,
Tom went to date her,
They went to the stream with no name,
So I took their path the same,
Tom put his finger to his lips,
He had fins and his fingertips,
As I was walking home in disgrace,
A big blowhole squirted in my face,
Out came a baby mermaid,
Her hair was a beautiful jade,
The mermaid told me not to tell
And handed me a beautiful shell.

Olivia Dommett (10)
St Mary's RC School, Falmouth

My Cat

Tarzan my cat,
Is very fat,
He rolls in the mud,
He catches mice and birds.

He thinks this pleases
But he just teases.

I love my fat furry cat,
Miaow

Jack Wallis (8)
St Mary's RC School, Falmouth

The Merry Maid Of Zennor

A veil of mysterious Cornish mist
Hangs low over a brown and barren landscape,
Hiding untold secrets - long forgotten!
Surrounding precious treasures,
A raging blue explosion of the calling sea.

Down in the deadly dark depths,
Lurk lost and unfortunate ghostly souls,
Often wandering the desolate cliffs,
I think of stories of my ancestor - Tom,
Gazing, staring, pondering, what mystery lies there.

The mystery of Tom Taskis and his merry maid,
Between the white horses galloping in,
I glimpse a face, a smile, a hand, a wave!

And there I saw a shimmering merry maid,
In the depths of the huge blue ocean,
I was sure I'd seen her before,
When Tom Taskis disappeared forever.

Zachy went to peep over the cliff,
Suddenly a blowhole shot up,
There was a merry child of Zennor.

Zachy picked it up and held it aloft,
Suddenly it disappeared!
But I knew where it had gone,
It had gone back to live a life with the other merry maids,
Beneath the shimmering ocean,
Under Zennor's blanket of truth.

Megan Christophers (10)
St Mary's RC School, Falmouth

Best Places

Dawlish beach, where rocks and shells tickle your feet
And waves shatter on rocks,
A chilled out ice cream tops it all off,
On my dad's boat in Salcombe,
Secret beaches, sunlit views,
Just look out and scan,
The horizon for boats and sand dunes.

Friends,
Snowboarding with skiing,
Mountainsides and cliff edges,
With the sound of silence,
Countryside,
Windy roads and empty fields,
Lovely barns with a rustling of trees.

All places are good and great,
But the best is in my garden,
All alone.

Jed Maiden (11)
St Peter's School, Lympstone

Best Places

My bed,
When getting in and
You feel snuggly and warm,
Our caravan,
When you go to bed on a
Cold, wintry night,
Woodbury Common,
Cycling around in the leaves,
Sliding down the hills on your bottom,
Making snowmen in the snow
And also having snowball fights,
My grandad's swimming pool,
Watching the sun set in the summer
And playing games in the pool,
Spain, swimming in the sea,
Going sailing and jumping
Off the side of the boat,
Eating hot chicken and pizza,
Going on the Broads,
Watching my brother sail the
Boat in the rain, sailing in the dinghy,
But the best place of all,
Is home.

Polly Authers (10)
St Peter's School, Lympstone

Best Places

The River Exe, when the boat is launched,
The water is so refreshing,
On a hot summer's day,
Meadows and fields,
The smell of fresh grass,
Buttercups amongst the long grass,
Woodburry Common,
Dogs and horses,
Running around chasing smells,
Scotland,
The frosted grass,
People wrapped up in scarves, gloves and hats,
Turf,
The smell of mud,
Swans, gracefully swimming.

Abbie Gall (11)
St Peter's School, Lympstone

Best Places

Polzeath Beach, walking with throbbing feet,
Using your muscles when they're dying down,
Surfing on huge waves,
Looking down on the people resting,
Dartmoor, sliding down the mossy rock pools,
Into the bottom of the water,
Swimming round and round in the cold, refreshing water,
France, skiing, looking down on the professionals
And sliding down the slippery slopes,
Whipe out when hit a hump,
Speeding down, spraying snow,
France is the best place to go.

Ben Hancock (11)
St Peter's School, Lympstone

Best Places

Dartmoor,
Letter boxes hidden away,
Climbing rocks,
Picnicking in the long grass,
Woodbury Common,
Large places to run around in,
Peaceful and quiet,
Never ever busy,
Autumn,
Lots of leaves to kick along the ground,
Cool breezes rush past your face,
My birthday full of presents and joy,
Canada,
My cousin's house,
Winter snow spread across the floor,
Friendly faces,
Exmouth beach,
Soft sand between my toes,
Salty sea to swim in,
Amazing sand sculptures,
But when all is said and done,
The best place is home.

Carragh Martineau (11)
St Peter's School, Lympstone

Best Places

Sea, when getting in and it is cold,
But knowing that your friend is too scared to come in,
Beaches, walking through shallow water
And listening to the seagulls,
Squawking and seeing them float
Gently on the seabed,
Fishing, when you know you're not going to catch anything,
But pushing your mum into the sea is fun.

Rebecca Bertrand (11)
St Peter's School, Lympstone

Best Places

Swimming pools, a place to cool off on a hot day,
Jumping in and feeling,
The cool water rush over you,
Grandparents' house,
Work shed,
With so many things to fiddle with,
Theme parks,
Massive roller coasters,
Then little tiny slides
And fresh candyfloss,
Fizzy drinks,
The time you're allowed them most,
The beach,
On a warm, sunny day,
Building sandcastles and digging holes,
But after all that,
For me,
The *best* place is home.

David Salmon (10)
St Peter's School, Lympstone

Best Places

Dartmoor, overlooking the fresh green grass,
The prickles and trees,
The sea on a calm day when the sun is rising,
My caravan with the CD booming,
At Spitchwick witch jumping into the clear water,
At the airport waiting to fly,
At home in my bed.

George Shoulder (11)
St Peter's School, Lympstone

Best Places

Skiing, floating down the diamond snow,
Slicing it up like a Christmas cake,
Feeling the wind freezing on your face,
School, chasing around on a cold winter's day,
All wrapped up like a birthday present,
Budleigh Beach, hearing the waves crash against the pebbles,
Swallowing them up like an eagle with its prey,
Sprinting, hearing the cheers of the anxious crowd,
Feeling something good bubbling up inside you,
Hearing the bang of the ferocious starting gun,
Heart pounding like a sleepless lion,
I love all these places,
But when I come to think of it,
My best place is home.

Lucy Parsons (11)
St Peter's School, Lympstone

Best Places

Woodbury Common,
When getting to it istough,
Watching my dogs run through the grass,
Pays for my lost breath,
My grandad's house,
With that fresh fruit smell,
The shingle on a beach,
Rough below my feet,
Seaweed and the freshwater scent,
My own little garden,
When I'm upset,
Lying down,
In my garden,
Watching the clouds
Go by.

Joshua Williamson (10)
St Peter's School, Lympstone

Best Places

Watching sunsets on a hill,
Listening to a bird sing a sweet song,
Going down the park to play a game,
Walking down the village for a lemonade.

Hot Italy, swimming in the lake,
Going through the Caribbean on a cruise,
Ice creams when you chose,
Swimming with dolphins, stingray, fish.

A summer's day on the beach,
Snowball fights in France,
Crispy orange autumn leaves,
Watching different shapes.

But finally I think
Where is the best place to be?
I couldn't really think,
I know, with all my family,
That's the best place to be.

Florence Hart (10)
St Peter's School, Lympstone

Best Places

Portuguese beaches, with the sun on your back,
The warm sand beneath your feet,
The sea to see how far you can swim,
North Yorkshire moors,
Walking through heather,
With big walking boots,
For splashing in puddles,
Dark woods at night,
Windy and wet,
The swishing of the trees,
Whilst you're telling ghost stories,
Camping at school,
My first time in a tent,
As cold as the frost itself,
Most places are good,
From theme parks to the wood,
My dad is the moors,
My mum's the city,
But my favourite place is home in bed.

Jamie Kenyon (11)
St Peter's School, Lympstone

Fear

Fear is a coin stuck in a drain,
Fear is an iceberg melting in an ocean,
Fear is being lost and deserted,
Fear is an everlasting steep hill,
Fear is a maze court up in your mind,
Fear is being alone in darkness,
Fear is panic and horror,
Fear is losing something special,
Fear is water draining down a plughole,
Fear is still and spooky,
Fear is a misty figure in blackness.

Daisy Kensett (10)
Thurlestone All Saints CE Primary School, Kingsbridge

What Is Fear?

Fear is losing your family,
Fear is being an orphan,
Fear is being alone,
Fear is being lost forever and never being found,
Fear is having nobody to love you,
Fear is not being protected,
Fear is not being noticed,
Fear is suffering,
Fear is losing your sight,
Fear is growing older,
Fear is having no home.
Fear is dying.

That's fear.

Beth Yeoman (10)
Thurlestone All Saints CE Primary School, Kingsbridge

Fear

What is fear?
Fear is being alone,
Fear is being an orphan,
Fear is having no friends,
Fear is being lost in a forest,
Fear is being in a deserted street,
Fear is thinking of suffering,
Fear is losing something precious,
Fear is like having a hollow heart,
Fear is not knowing what is going to happen to you,
Fear is death,
Fear is darkness,
Fear is like being trapped in a cupboard.

Ben Appleyard (10)
Thurlestone All Saints CE Primary School, Kingsbridge

Fear

Fear is a hollow stomach,
Fear is a lost brain,
Fear is a stuck leg,
Fear, an incredible strain.

Fear follows footprints,
Fear bites rock,
Fear follows market cows
And any livestock.

Fear rustles granite,
Fear breaks joy,
Fear is whipped poverty,
From a foreign boy.

Fear peels off skin
And nobody can tell,
Until the very moment,
When you smell the fearful smell.

George Fountain (11)
Thurlestone All Saints CE Primary School, Kingsbridge

Flattering Daffodils

Daffodils waving in the rich colours,
Afraid that the magnificent music of the wind might stop,
Flowers, you would have expected less from, shimmering flowers,
Flattering the humans, radiantly and softly,
Outshine the gold rays of sun,
Dazzling so brightly on the grassy hills,
I feel the wavy winds blowing,
Lighting the world all around,
Daffodils have the most amazing shine.

Hugo Walliss (10)
Thurlestone All Saints CE Primary School, Kingsbridge

The Midnight Sky

As I look at the deep sky,
Like a frozen silent lake
And the ice is just about to seal up,
Just then, you hear something,
A crack breaks the ice,
The noise comes back again
And the noise sounds like -
Like - hmm.

A thick layer of fog,
A ghost haunting the midnight sky,
A fossil shimmering like the moon,
A black, dark chocolate bar,
A snowflake dropping to the ground,
A see-through frost.

Charlotte Holland (10)
Thurlestone All Saints CE Primary School, Kingsbridge

Blossom

Blossom falling from the tree,
Blossom falling to the ground,
Blossom on a tree,
Blossom on the ground,
Blossom for you and me,
Blossom on a tree,
Blossom on the ground,
Blossom all pink and blue to share,
Blossom on a tree,
Blossom on the ground,
Blossom for you and me,
Blossom flying everywhere.

Lauren Yeoman (9)
Thurlestone All Saints CE Primary School, Kingsbridge

Fear

Fear is being alone in the dark,
Fear is being trapped,
Fear is being alone,
Fear is losing someone close to you,
Fear is being angry,
Fear is death,
Fear is getting lost,
Fear is the past, present and future,
Fear is dying a long, painful death,
Fear is losing my friends,
Fear is being lost,
Fear is being deaf,
Fear of the future,
Fear is no one to look after you,
Fear is being scared,
Fear is a feeling,
Fear is getting old,
Fear is a thunderstorm,
Fear is cancer,
Fear kills,
Fear is not a good thing,
Fear is not clear,
Fear is fear.

Toby Yeoman (11)
Thurlestone All Saints CE Primary School, Kingsbridge

The Magnificent Kitten

My kitten is fluffy like a fluffy scarf,
His fur is like a tortoiseshell,
His nose is like a bright pink pig,
His eyes are like the Torquay sea,
He represents a fluffy tortoise without a shell,
I will love him forever.

Eleanor Rose Soole (9)
Thurlestone All Saints CE Primary School, Kingsbridge

Fear

Fear is being homeless,
Fear is losing your family,
Fear is dying of hunger,
Fear is murder by someone you know.

Fear is cancer,
Fear is suffocating,
Fear is heart disease,
Fear is not being able to walk.

Fear is child abuse,
Fear is being blind,
Fear is being abandoned,
Fear is taking drugs.

Fear is being threatened by a knife,
Fear is being bitten by a snake,
Fear is having brain damage,
Fear is not being able to hear.

Fear is being kidnapped,
Fear is having a broken neck,
Fear is the future,
Fear is losing your friends.

Fear is your imagination,
Fear is the doors opening by the wind like a ghost,
Fear is knowing you're going to die soon,
Fear is your nightmares.

Fear is being alone in the dark,
Fear is drowning in the water,
Fear is choking,
Fear is being pinned to the wall by bullies.

Fear is being hurt by your friends.

Maria Makepeace (10)
Thurlestone All Saints CE Primary School, Kingsbridge

What Is Fear?

Fear is being alone in darkness,
Fear is losing your best friend,
Fear is not being loved,
Fear is not being able to walk or talk,
Fear is losing your friend in an accident.

Fear of two rhinos grinding the path before you,
Fear of having a burglar in your house,
Fear of dying alone,
Fear of walking past a group of teenagers, who look suspicious,
Fear of not having any food or drink,
Fear of not having a home.

Fear is when your pet has died from an operation,
Fear is not having any friends,
Fear is being bullied by teenagers.

Fear is unwelcome but has made its way past.

Kelly Parkinson (10)
Thurlestone All Saints CE Primary School, Kingsbridge

Fear

What is fear?
Fear is a lost child in a wartorn country,
Fear of the thin line between life and death,
Fear is being lost in the Minotaur's labyrinth,
Fear of a hoodie in a lonely street,
Fear is a desperate struggle for life,
Fear is being forgotten,
Fear is dying slowly,
Fear of not knowing what lies behind closed doors,
Fear is always there whether you like it or not!

Jack Antoniades (11)
Thurlestone All Saints CE Primary School, Kingsbridge

What Is Fear?

Fear is being alone in an empty street,
Fear is like getting followed by a gangster,
Fear is getting kidnapped,
Fear,
Fear,
What is fear?

Fear is the Devil breathing into the bitter air,
Fear is being alone with no one to talk to,
Fear is being lost,
Fear,
Fear,
What is fear?

Fear is losing your family,
Fear is getting stranded on an island,
Fear is knowing you are going to die very soon,
Fear,
Fear,
What is fear?

Hayley Betteridge (10)
Thurlestone All Saints CE Primary School, Kingsbridge

Fear

Fear is losing a friend,
Fear is living on the streets with strangers,
Fear is being put into a home,
Fear is a brother being in a car crash,
Fear is being kidnapped,
Fear is being alone when your mum has gone out,
Fear is having a bad dream that could come true,
Fear is being killed by a loony,
Fear is having some sort of attack,
Fear is moving into your new house,
Fear is having a car accident.

Thomas Lee (11)
Thurlestone All Saints CE Primary School, Kingsbridge

Fear

Fear is being alone,
Fear is being in the cold,
Fear is being in darkness,
Fear is being with a bunch of
Suspicious looking teenagers,
Fear is being with some people you don't know,
Fear is thinking people will leave you,
Fear is thinking people will not love you,
Fear is thinking death is near,
Fear is thinking of the storms that are waiting for you,
Fear is thinking of emptiness,
Fear is something painful,
Fear is something dreadful,
Fear is something no one wants,
Fear is something everyone has,
Fear is something that comes whether you like it or not.

Georgia Clipsham (10)
Thurlestone All Saints CE Primary School, Kingsbridge

Fear

Fear is being at death's door,
Fear is your only hope being snuffed out in an instant,
Fear is being alone in a dark empty room,
Fear is the feeling of an empty presence,
Fear is the wind in the trees,
Fear is the sound of footsteps behind you,
Fear is pain,
Fear is death,
Fear is anger,
Fear is emptiness,
Fear is losing the light of your life,
Fear is no hope for the future.

Alex Gubbay (10)
Thurlestone All Saints CE Primary School, Kingsbridge

Fear

Fear is losing your family,
Fear is being alone,
Fear is something that's there
But you don't know it.

Fear is a mind full of dread,
Fear is poison running through your veins,
Fear is crying for help but,
You can never be heard.

Fear is to face the world at its dreaded times,
Fear is a grounded spirit,
Fear is death,
Fear is . . .
What is fear?

Laura Sutton (10)
Thurlestone All Saints CE Primary School, Kingsbridge

Fear

What is fear?
Fear is a chicken being slaughtered,
Fear is being lost in a shop,
Fear is seeing shapes in the dark night,
Fear is a gang walking towards you,
Fear is someone following you,
Fear is seeing something move under your bed,
Fear is being lost outside in the night,
Fear is being lost in a city,
Fear is sadness' best friend.

Lloyd Lee (10)
Thurlestone All Saints CE Primary School, Kingsbridge

Fear

Fear,
What is fear?
Fear is what we are scared of,
Fear,
Fear is a kidnapped child,
Fear, bigger than phobias,
Alone, alone with fear.

No one's there, but in our minds,
Fear,
When you hear something in the night,
Fear,
Fear is death and being left with no one,
Being left is fear, left to fend for yourself,
Emotions overruling common sense,
That's fear,
Alone, alone with fear.

People leaving never coming back,
Being left is fear,
Still, in a coma, can hear but can't speak,
In their mind, don't pull the plug please don't,
But still they might,
Fear,
Fear is an empty heart that no longer cares,
Fear is ending up poor like people they see on TV,
Then you would care, too late but you would care,
Fear is being swallowed by nightmares,
Fear, fear, fear,
Alone, alone with fear.

Lucy Peters (11)
Thurlestone All Saints CE Primary School, Kingsbridge

What Is Fear?

Fear is on a sinking ship,
Fear is war,
Fear is trying to get down off a tree,
Fear is prison,
Fear is thirst when there is nothing to drink,
Fear is being alone,
Fear is watching a scary movie,
Fear is being trapped,
Fear is facing a dangerous animal,
Fear is being abandoned,
Fear is falling from a tall height.

Fear is a creepy spider,
Fear is about to go on show,
Fear is darkness,
Fear is a shadow,
Fear is a tsunami,
Fear is losing someone,
Fear is being invaded,
Fear is the next day,
Fear is blood out of your heart,
Fear is the future.

Fear is telling a secret,
Fear is your dying day.

What else is fear?
Fear is fear itself . . .

Annie Rankin (10)
Thurlestone All Saints CE Primary School, Kingsbridge

What Is Fear?

What is fear?
A mixture of things,
Fear is an illness,
Fear is a blacked-out city,
Fear is loneliness,
Fear is not wanting to lose someone.

What is fear?
Fear is lots of things,
Fear is what you're scared of,
Fear is a different language,
Fear is a blur of the future,
Fear is a hollow tree stump.

What is fear?
Fear is loads of things,
Fear is sometimes called a phobia,
Fear is something eating you up,
Fear is being abandoned by your family,
Fear is a bubbling cauldron inside you about to explode.

What is fear?
Fear is an amazing cupboard of toys,
Fear is darkness with no light,
Fear is an unhappy death,
Fear is a sinking ship,
Fear is great and powerful.

What is fear?
Fear is a great trunk of things,
Fear is a snake twisting and turning in your insides,
Fear is a hungry lion chewing at your insides,
Fear is an empty, abandoned room,
Fear is fear.

What is fear?

Frances Pope (10)
Thurlestone All Saints CE Primary School, Kingsbridge

Fear

Fear is when you're scared of something happening or
Something you think might happen.

Fear is being alone in the dark,
Fear is being lost and not found,
Fear is having nothing,
Fear is losing your only hope,
Fear is the loss of a loved one,
Fear is knowing you'll never see someone again,
Fear is knowing you'll never be young again,
Fear comes with worry,
Fear comes with despair,
But fear is just an emotion,
A cold emotion that strikes everyone,
Now and then,
But is it?
Is that all fear is?

Heather Chadwick (10)
Thurlestone All Saints CE Primary School, Kingsbridge

Waterfall

Waterfall trickling down,
No matter what shape or size,
At the bottom there's a polar bear playing,
With what? You cannot tell,
Don't go to the top,
You'll fall,
The white dragon,
It'll take you down.

Everyone says it's like,
A beautiful multicoloured rainbow,
Thousands of sparkling crystals falling,
The night sky brightening up the pond.

Emma Wright (10)
Thurlestone All Saints CE Primary School, Kingsbridge

Fear

Fear is being left in darkness,
Fear is losing all hope,
Fear is death,
Fear is great hunger,
Fear is thirst greater than ever,
Fear is cold,
Fear is death of friends and family,
Fear is being lost.

Fear of danger,
Fear of burning skin,
Fear of war,
Fear of drowning,
Fear of the future.

Fear is curved reality,
Fear is deep,
Fear is disaster.

Fear is sorrow,
Fear is heavy,
Fear is cunning,
Fear is opaque.

Tim Fenton-Jones (10)
Thurlestone All Saints CE Primary School, Kingsbridge

Fear

Fear is a child with no protector,
Fear is an iced-up body, shivering,
Fear is a paralysed shock icing its way up,
Fear is being lost in emotions,
Fear is a deadly scare,
Fear of snakes slithering up you and forcing venom into you,
Fear of bees with devil-tailed stings,
Fear of losing someone you love,
Fear of closing your eyes but not waking.

Rosie Price (11)
Thurlestone All Saints CE Primary School, Kingsbridge

Fear

Fear is losing a friend or a person in your family,
Fear is death,
Fear is darkness,
Fear is being lost,
Fear is being hurt,
Fear is growing old,
Fear is getting ill,
Fear is losing your pet,
Fear kills you,
Fear is bad,
Fear is being cold,
Fear no one loving you,
Fear is fear.

Fear is seeing shadows,
Fear is heavy,
Fear is dying,
Fear is the future.

Simon Hackley (10)
Thurlestone All Saints CE Primary School, Kingsbridge

Me And My Sis

Me and my sis are always fighting,
Scratch, scratch, scratch and of course some biting,
Swearing naaa, we never swear,
But we certainly argue on what we are going to wear,
So, you better object to a baby,
Because they're normally very crazy.

Jemima Booth (9)
Thurlestone All Saints CE Primary School, Kingsbridge

Fear

What is fear?
Fear is boiling hot lava racing towards you,
What is fear?
Fear is great pain,
What is fear?
Fear is a disease spreading through your body,
What is fear?
Fear is your last breath,
What is fear?
Fear is death in war,
What is fear?
Fear is death again and again and again,
What is fear?
Fear is being lost and not found,
What is fear?
Fear is darkness deep in you.

Joe Lywood (10)
Thurlestone All Saints CE Primary School, Kingsbridge

The Magnificent Bird

My bird is golden like the gifts from the wise men,
His beak is like the black night sky,
His call is like a thousand vibrations sent across the Earth,
His feathers are like a puppy's fur, soft and smooth,
He resembles a king, so strong and determined,
I will plant a big oak tree for him to nest in.

Hannah Tait (9)
Thurlestone All Saints CE Primary School, Kingsbridge